D1124839

SHADOW OF THE SUN

BASED ON AN INSPIRING TRUE STORY

MARNEY BLOM

Shadow of the Sun
Copyright © 2020 Marney Blom
www.shadowofthesun.org

All rights reserved. The use of any part of this publication reproduced,
transmitted in any form or by any means, electronic, mechanical, photocopying,
recording or otherwise, or stored in a retrieval system, without the prior written
consent of the publisher — or, in the case of photocopying or other reprographic
copying, a license from the Canadian Copyright Licensing agency — is an
infringement of the copyright law.

Blom, Marney
shadow of the sun: a novel / Marney Blom

Book ISBN: 978-0-9781036-1-3
eBook ISBN: 978-0-9781036-2-0

In chapters where songs and hymns have been quoted, copyright guidelines
concerning "fair use" of material have been observed and no explicit permission
for reprinted quotes is necessary. In chapters where photos have been used,
permission has been obtained.

Scripture quotations are from The Holy Bible, English Standard Version. ESV®
Text Edition: 2016. Copyright © 2001 by Crossway Bibles, a publishing ministry
of Good News Publishers. Used by permission. All rights reserved.

Toviyahu Publishing is a division of Acts News Network, Inc.
www.actsnewsnetwork.com

Contact:
shadowofthesunbook@gmail.com

Cover design by Ken Jansen
Layout, format and page design by Writing Momentum LLC

Printed and bound in Canada

100%   PCF   BIO GAS   PERMANENT

REVIEWS

"*Shadow of the Sun* brings to life a heroic Dutch family in the midst of the horrors of World War II. But this is a universal story of godly faith and trust in the valley of the shadow of death. Their crucible in the furnace of affliction — that reads like a movie — is a timely lesson to trust God even in the most desperate situation. This family's steely love for one another will inspire, encourage and warm your heart like it did mine. And perhaps like me you'll end up with tears in your eyes at the miracle of God's everlasting faithfulness."

— **Chris Mitchell**
CBN News Middle East Bureau Chief

"*Shadow of the Sun* draws us close into the drama of the unspeakably high price that has been paid for freedom and democracy. Through the true-life story of a missionary family torn apart and brutalized by WWII, this historical novel deeply touches the soul in a most needed way."

— **Lorna Dueck**
Fmr. CEO of Crossroads, Yes TV, Tricord Media,
TV Host for *Context: Beyond the Headlines*

Marney Blom has penned a gripping, must-read story based on true events of her ancestors. With the backdrop of southeast Asia during World War II, the story engages the heart and shares inspiring lessons for today. Most of all, the story poses a question to each of us, *what are we living for*?

Marney is a gifted storyteller. I love a great book you can't put down -- one that stirs the emotions and offers "take away" truths. You will find these qualities and more in *Shadow of the Sun*. Grab your tissues, take time to absorb the anointed narration, and prepare to be changed!

— **Patricia Bootsma**
Co-Senior Leader, Catch the Fire Canada

My cousin Marney paints a vivid picture of a missionary family's suffering under Japanese oppression in WWII. The very personal accounts of suffering in Japanese prison camps in the letters our granddad wrote to grandma are deeply moving. How did they manage to survive and how is it possible to have so little bitterness toward their enemy and perhaps even towards the God whom they were serving in their mission work? Where was He in all this? Yet, right in the middle of these desperate circumstances they find Him. The story left me with a loss for words, wondering at the grace of God and the fact that I exist. I warmly recommend this book.

— **Menno A. Helmus**
Founder, Team Leader, Vineyard Benelux

An amazing book that grabs your heart from the first page to the last! We travel with the Giliam family each step of the way through the horrors of war, feeling their pain, tasting their fears, yet finding the true Light in the midst of terrible darkness.

The book answers the question God is asking each of us today: If I am all you have, am I enough? This family found the answer through severe trial.

— **Ian Ross**
Executive Director, Father Heart Ministry

This is a gripping page-turner and a story vividly and skillfully woven by their granddaughter, who has employed her grandfather's unsent letters, miraculously rescued and preserved. *Shadow of the Sun* not only captivates through its accounts of miraculous and divine protection, but exposes the inner workings of the soul in the face of severe suffering. It is not possible to read this true story without doing one's own soul-searching and re-evaluation of priorities.

— **Wayne Hilsden**
Co-Founder and Pres. King of Kings Community Jerusalem,
Pres. FIRM (Fellowship of Israel Related Ministries)

CONTENTS

I dedicate this book to my late parents,
Hans Blom and Ineke Blom-Giliam.

I miss you.

And to Miss Dawn Roherty, my high school English teacher at the
Peoples Christian Academy (née the Paul B. Smith Academy) in
Toronto, who after reading one of my essays asked if English was my
second language!

Proof — nothing is impossible with God.

FOREWORD

More than 50 years of my life have been dedicated to one cause, and one cause only: missions!

As the leader of an Asian front-line mission, we have ventured into some of the most restrictive countries: Vietnam and Cambodia during their war-torn years, China amidst its catastrophic cultural revolutions of the 60's, Outer Mongolia, Nepal, the Himalayas, and Pakistan. We witnessed tremendous harvests and without exception, they came only after great hardship and grave difficulties.

You may ask, "Why this boldness?" I would readily reply, it was on account of the books I read as a teenager in Hong Kong of missionaries — stories that followed Dr. Hudson Taylor into China's most demanding interiors. Those books inspired me, challenged me, molded me and I reckon had the same effect on many youngsters.

Now I am in my 70's, yet Marney Blom's *Shadow of the Sun* still has the same effect on me. I read the manuscript over the Christmas holiday, but it was not really "reading," per se. It was actually more like watching an action-packed movie. I was gripped!

Marney is indeed a very gifted storyteller and movie maker. After all, she's a journalist and a television reporter.

This book is a potential missionary classic in the making.

— Rev. Dr. David Wang
President Emeritus, Asian Outreach International

PROLOGUE

DJATIBARANG, WEST JAVA, MARCH 1942

Oppressive, sweltering heat settled on the armed Dutch fighters hiding in the trees along Djatibarang's riverbank. A tall Frisian soldier swatted a buzzing mosquito with one hand. In the other, he held a detonator. Pensive and focused, he waited for the command that would signal the destruction of the towering railway bridge before him. It was March 1942, and the Japanese Imperial army had advanced rapidly across the Dutch East Indies island of Java. All able-bodied Dutchmen living in the colony had been called up for military duty, even citizens like missionary school headmaster Menno Giliam.

Perched on a lookout twenty meters away, a young sergeant received the signal from the munitions crew and flagged Menno: All clear! Menno slammed the detonator handle. The sound was deafening, the explosions spectacular. Wood, metal, smoke, and fumes shot skyward as sections of the once heavily traveled railroad folded and collapsed like dominoes into the river below.

Their heads protected under military-green helmets with leather back flaps, the soldiers ducked, taking cover from the sudden rain of railroad debris. An eerie quiet followed. Soon the thick dust parted revealing only the bridge's concrete foundations standing.

Awestruck by the power of the blasts, Menno wiped beads of sweat from his brow with the back of his arm. "Good!" he said, leaning into a young, ruddy soldier next to him as they both stood up to observe their achievement. "That should slow down the Japs — for now."

The intensity of the assignment gave way to celebration. The men, thrilled with the success of their mission, rose from their hiding places to exchange triumphant shouts and collect their equipment. Menno, smiling, turned to pack the detonator, but his eye caught something on the opposite ridge. Movement?

"Get down! Get down!" He shouted. "Could be Japs!"

The men dropped for cover, rifles cocked. Breathing heavily, they feared their slightest movement could expose them.

Too late! A salvo of bullets ignited from the rifles of the highly disciplined, khaki-clad Japanese rapidly descending into the river's gully. The small company of Dutch army recruits scrambled for cover. Terrified and outnumbered, they quickly abandoned all efforts to return fire.

1

GO WITH GOD

The thick, pungent odor of grazing cows mingled with the moist westerly rolling in from the North Sea. Menno's blue eyes squinted as he leaned into the wind and pedaled his well-worn bicycle, intent on outpacing the rain. He breathed hard and moved fast, racing toward the tiny Frisian village of Boazum in northern Holland.

The pot-holed, bullet-straight road intersected softly rolling farmland crisscrossed by rows of swollen canals. Studded with the occasional towering windmill, the road rose and fell gently with the curve of an arched wooden bridge, its planks echoing a hollow rhythm under his bicycle wheels. Without losing speed, he swerved sharply to avoid a farmer's cart pulled by a magnificent, jet-black Friesian mare. Menno was on a mission.

He steered his bike down the narrow cobblestone road leading into the tiny village of quaint brick homes. Windblown, he raced toward the cobbler's shop, leapt off his rolling bike and leaned it against the red brick wall.

A hand-carved brass bell clanged as he burst through the shop door. "Albert! Flor can go!" Behind the rustic counter a gentle-faced stocky cobbler, two decades older, glanced up as Menno yanked off his cap. A flurry of thick curls cascaded down his forehead.

Preoccupied with stitching a broken shoe, Albert raised an eyebrow and peered over his glasses. "Flor passed the medical examinations!" Menno exclaimed. "The Frisian mission said she is fit for the Indies. We can go!"

"Menno, *jongen* [young man]. That is fantastic! Even with all the trouble she's had with her back?" The stocky cobbler rose from his bench to give him a hearty handshake. Menno lurched forward to embrace him.

"But ... don't you and Flor need to get married first?"

"Yes! And it won't be long! Within a fortnight, I reckon," Menno beamed. "And then, if all goes to plan, we'll sail for the Indies the following week."

"*Fan herte lokwinske* [Congratulations]!" The Frisian cobbler was elated. He grinned as he returned to his workbench.

Since the Giliam home shared the same building with Albert's shop and home, he had watched Menno work hard to qualify for overseas missions. The son of a poor milkman, Menno was expected to support the family once he completed grade school. When he finished working hard all day in the fields, he chose instead to study late into the night by oil lamp, in his tiny room in the attic of a barn.

Four years later he passed the government certification exams and became a teacher through correspondence courses. It took another two years for him to earn a degree in secondary school education, followed by his headmaster certification. Against the odds, he had achieved his educational goals by his mid-twenties — unthinkable for someone of his socio-economic status.

Menno then set his sights on the distant, exotic land of the Dutch East Indies (now Indonesia). He had worked hard for a vocation that would allow him to travel, explore the world and give the uneducated an opportunity to learn about the central, most important aspect of his life — God.

There was one requirement, however, that hindered Menno from serving abroad with the Frisian Church Mission. In 1928 it was unfitting for a young, unmarried, male candidate to serve overseas. The lovely, yet delicate, 18-year-old Flor Zijlstra, whom Menno longed to betroth, did not appear to have the constitution for the rigors of missionary life in the Dutch East Indies. She had repeatedly failed the mandatory medical examinations. Although Flor's back still occasionally gave her grief, on this day, the mission's medical board had deemed her fit to go.

"Albert, I'm going to miss this place." Menno panned the tiny shop where he and Albert had spent many hours together. His eyes caught the skillful workmanship of a black, high-heeled flapper shoe on the counter. "I've enjoyed our talks and watching the master at work."

With a clunk, Albert dropped the half-sewn shoe, stood up and wandered to the shop window. His back to Menno, he gazed through the glass to mask his sadness. Rain pelted a passenger in a small watercraft that journeyed through the canal behind the back of the shop. "Are you sure Flor can handle living in the Indies? All those malaria mosquitoes and the heat? It could be difficult for her."

Menno laid a hand on Albert's shoulder to reassure him. He knew his friend would miss him and perceived that he was trying to dissuade him. "Don't you worry. By my side, she'll be just fine."

From a doorway at the back of the shop, a melodic female voice called, "Albert! *Koffee!*"

The cobbler sighed. His eyes met Menno's eager gaze and turned downward as he shuffled toward the door. Pausing, he lifted his head and inhaled the scent of the rich Java brew drifting into the shop. "Be there in a minute, *schat* [darling]!" He turned back to Menno. "I've heard rumblings from the Indies. Not all the

17

islanders are happy under Dutch rule. If one day they demand their independence, things could get ugly."

Albert studied the young schoolmaster. "And, of course, there's Nippon ... "

The sudden, dark shift in Albert's normally jovial disposition made Menno uneasy. "Nippon?"

"Rumor has it," Albert leaned forward, "Japanese shopkeepers in the Indies could be spies. It's no secret they have their eyes on the Dutch Indies — and its wealth."

"Ha!" Menno laughed as he ran a finger along the top of a repaired shoe displayed on the counter. *That's it!* he thought. *He's afraid we'll be in danger.*

"Albert! I've worked six years to become a school headmaster, and now God has given me a wife willing to move halfway around the world. I am going." Menno's eyes burned with conviction. "Besides, you're forgetting something. Flor and I — we don't go alone. We go with God!"

"I know." Albert shook his head and smiled at his stubborn, young, Frisian friend. "When you put your mind to something, nothing's gonna get in your way. But ... I'm just not sure it's gonna be easy."

The heavens seemed to agree. Thunder clapped overhead as the rain intensified.

∾

THE CAMERA FLASH MOMENTARILY BLINDED MENNO AND FLOR AS they stood poised and earnest for pictures on their wedding day. September 3, 1928 had finally arrived — a day that held great promise. With the ceremony at the Frisian Reformed Church in Boazum completed earlier in the day, the family gathered for wedding photos at a local studio.

A head shorter than Menno, Flor turned her face, chiseled and beautiful like porcelain, toward his and shyly reached to adjust her new husband's tie. The drop-waist, knee-length wedding dress she had sewn herself, draped modestly over her slender form.

Their eyes met in a tender embrace. Six-foot-tall Menno, dignified and handsome, sporting his characteristic wild shock of dark, curly hair, savored his new wife's attention. "I'm going to take care of you," he whispered.

"I know." Flor trusted her husband.

The newlywed couple straightened and resumed their solemn pose for the camera. A few more flashes and the holy matrimony would be immortalized forever.

FLOR HELD HER HAT AGAINST A SUDDEN, COLD GUST OF WIND AS A Dutch flag flapped madly overhead. It was late September and the S.S. Tjerimai prepared to set sail from Rotterdam. Menno and Flor leaned on the ship's railing to catch a final glimpse of the pier below. Smartly dressed gentlemen in double-breasted suits, and ladies in fox-collared jackets, some with rambunctious children in tow, crowded the wooden deck waving at friends and relatives below.

Bhaaaaahhmm! The ship's horn bellowed a low, hollow warning in preparation for departure. Flor's eyes filled with tears. "Menno, I'm going to miss everyone," she said, as she waved to the crowd.

"*Schat*, we are going to see the world!" Menno wrapped protective arms around his new bride, drawing her close. He heard her angst but could not suppress his excitement.

"*Iedereen aan boord* [All aboard]!" The loudspeaker overhead crackled, and the captain's voice boomed.

The roar of the crowd's final good-bye rose as the ship pulled forward to begin the month-long journey to the Dutch East Indies island of Java.

Nearby squawking seagulls encircled an incoming wooden fishing craft as the chilly westerly picked up. The massive vessel inched away from the dock almost imperceptibly, its heavy hulk gliding out of the harbor into the dark, choppy North Sea.

2

THE MISSION

Gombong, Central Java, Dutch East Indies, Autumn 1941

Red clay-tiled and framed by a ten-arch veranda, the Dutch Christian Domestic School (*Christian Hollandse Inlandse School*), with 400 Javanese pupils, stood guarded by proud, looming Tamara palms on either side. Vibrant voices of hundreds of Indies school children singing the Dutch national anthem emanated from the immaculate, white stucco building. Regardless of how many times Menno, their respected headmaster, heard them sing, he never tired of it.

It had been thirteen years since his arrival in the Dutch East Indies, yet it still lived vividly in his mind. The culture shock was immediate. Energetic, dark-skinned Asians — forty million on the island of Java — conversed in mostly Chinese and Indies languages. The stifling heat and humidity, towering palms and rolling countryside were all a sharp contrast to the flat, tranquil farmland and quaint Dutch villages he and Flor had known all their lives.

Without delay, Menno was assigned a teaching position at a mission school in the tropical town of Keboemen (Kebumen). Acclimatization, language study and integration into the local culture had, at times, been difficult for the new missionaries, but by 1937 Menno had been promoted to the position of head-master at a small school in the mountainous region of Wonosobo.

Prior to Menno's posting, there had been few Christians of Chinese descent in the area, but over the years, in and around Wonosobo, the mission established ten Christian schools along with a large Christian church that was regularly filled with five hundred people. Life in Wonosobo, a picturesque town with cooler temperatures, was more bearable for Flor, and the family continued to grow.

By 1940, the Giliams had seven children, and Menno was newly appointed by the Frisian Church mission to develop schools in tropical Gombong, Central Java. It was a military town with a historic fort from the East-Indian Company days, and Fort van der Wijc, where soldiers trained for service in the Royal Netherlands Indies Army (*Koninklijk Nederlandsch-Indisch Leger, KNIL*).

Next door to the school was the colonial-style mission home where the Giliam family lived. Both buildings were situated on the Grote Postweg (the Great Post Road) at the town's main intersection. Further up the road was the Amboinese School with 150 pupils. Under Menno's tireless work and leadership, both schools flourished.

On that autumn day of 1941, the sound of an approaching 1930s black sedan rumbled above the children's singing and the inces-sant, low drone of wood-boring insects outside. Dr. de Jong, a tall, slender Dutchman in his late thirties, jumped from the passenger seat and opened the rear door for his two fair-haired boys.

"Hurry up *jongens* [boys]!" the man urged. "They've already started!"

The young voices from inside the school belted out the Dutch national anthem with passion: "*Dat ik doch vroom mag blijven, uw dienaar t'aller stond* [That I may remain pious, your servant always]."

The doctor's sons, eager to explore their exotic new environment, raced toward the building's arched entrance under an oversized Dutch flag and Roman numeral clock.

A crowded, white-washed school room throbbed with the energy of young, dark-haired Chinese-Indies students and three blond, Giliam children. Each stood neatly dressed behind a wooden double desk, the boys in cotton shirts and khaki shorts, the girls in an assortment of simple pastel dresses. At the front of the class, a petite Indonesian teacher wearing a traditional sarong and patterned blouse stood meekly under a stoic, formal portrait of their beloved Dutch matriarch, Queen Wilhelmina.

Towering next to her stood Menno, tanned and seasoned in his pressed white suit. A few gray strands peppered his voluminous head of dark hair. With fervor, he belted out the words of the precious anthem: " … *de tirannie verdrijven, die mij mijn hart door-wondt* [And defeat the tyranny, which pierces my heart]."

"Good morning students!" boomed the headmaster at the song's end.

"*Goedemorgen Tuan Besar* [Good morning Headmaster]!"

I was made for this, Menno silently reflected. It had been a long road to get to this stage in his career, but he had excelled with each new challenge.

"Children, I would like to introduce your new teacher, Mrs. Kartono. She comes highly qualified from Jakarta and I have every confidence she will do a wonderful job. Students, please welcome her."

"*Goedemorgen Mevrouw Kartono* [Good day, Mrs. Kartono]!" The new teacher bowed gracefully, shyly averting her eyes.

I'll leave you in her capable hands," Menno concluded and turned toward the door. "Good day students!"

"Goedemorgen Tuan Besar!"

Taking their cue, the students shuffled their wooden benches and seated themselves, while Menno strode confidently from the room.

Yelly, Menno's blonde, long-legged ten-year-old stood several inches taller than the sprightly Chinese-Indies children around her. Her thick braid swung across her shoulder as she tucked her dress under and sat down, just to bounce out of her seat squealing. A lumbering giant, male stag beetle had suddenly landed on her desk terrifying her. Giggles erupted across the room.

"Children! Children, calm down." A flustered Mrs. Kartono attempted to regain control.

Delighted by the awkward creature, an Indies boy quickly scooped it into his pocket and slid into his seat in the row beside her.

≈

"Look, *VADER* [Father]! Look!" shrieked the youngest son of the missionary doctor, pointing at the wall behind them. Both boys scrambled onto the bench in Menno's office in an attempt to catch the tiny earth-toned gecko scuttling out of reach. It was a small, welcome divergence until Headmaster Giliam arrived.

"*Go'e dag* [Good day] Dr. de Jong. I've been expecting you." Menno strode through the door, a hand extended.

"*Go'e dag* [Good day] *Meneer* [Mister] Giliam." Dr. de Jong stood to his feet to shake hands with Menno. "My sincere apologies for being late. A baby with malaria meant an early call."

"*Jongens* [Boys] sit down. Please!" The doctor reprimanded his boys for clamoring against the wall. As he so often did in church, the doctor instinctively pulled out a roll of King peppermints. Peeling back the wrapper, he motioned to the younger, Wouter, to take one and pass the roll to his older brother.

With the boys settled, Dr. de Jong pulled out folded documents from his breast pocket. "This is my oldest, Theo." He waved the papers in the boy's direction. "He's ten. And this is his brother Wouter, six. I believe these are the documents you requested." He held them out to Menno.

"*Jongens!* You're the same age as my two sons." Menno observed cheerfully, with casual familiarity. "Please Dr. de Jong. Please have a seat."

Settled behind his sprawling teak desk covered in neatly stacked paperwork, Menno examined the doctor's registration documents. "Everything seems to be in order," he confirmed, laying the papers down.

The physician wiped beads of sweat from his brow with a handkerchief. "I never imagined this kind of heat!"

Menno smiled. "We arrived thirteen years ago, and my wife still suffers terribly from the high temperatures and humidity."

Theo swatted a mosquito, killing it before it bit his arm. "*Vader*, is this the kind of mosquito that made the baby sick?" he asked, irritated.

"The needs here are great," offered Menno. "The islanders will keep you busy, Doctor." The Dutch health care system had introduced vaccinations against smallpox, but other diseases such as dysentery, malaria, cholera, and dengue fever had taken their toll on the locals.

"Excuse me, *Meneer* Giliam, two more applications." The face of Menno's gentle Indonesian school secretary appeared through the half-open door.

"Thank you," Menno motioned her in. "Please set them on my desk. And ... please show Theo and Wouter to their class."

The petite islander gracefully slipped into the room, placed two manila file folders atop an already-towering pile and gently beckoned the two boys to follow.

Still distracted by mosquitoes, Theo flailed at another while Wouter scratched the reddening bump on his leg. "So itchy!" he complained.

"Jongens," Menno sympathized, "It'll go away soon. You'll see."

The two young students ventured into their strange new school, following closely behind the secretary.

"Looks like the islanders are keeping the headmaster busy too," the doctor commented, pointing to the pile on Menno's desk.

Menno grinned. He was proud of the school. They had exceeded the enrolment goals of the Dutch Indies mission in a pioneering work that introduced hundreds of local children to the Gospel. The mission board was duly impressed with the determined young Frisian.

Menno paused a moment. He needed to select his words carefully.

Most of the Dutch nationals, who held senior positions in the large companies, the military, and government, regarded themselves as the upper class, and lived in grand houses. Menno and Flor felt the rigid Dutch colonial distinction keenly. The elite might socialize with the Javanese nobility, but not with Dutch nationals such as clerks and missionaries. Others, like the Chinese merchants they tolerated, and the islanders — people from the countryside who were mainly Muslim — they exploited as inexpensive labor.

While the children of Dutch families and elite Indonesians could afford to attend the prestigious European schools, most Indonesian, Chinese and Indian children attended second-tier schools, not unlike the mission schools.

"You do know the Dutch prefer *not* to educate their children with the locals?"

The physician nodded. "Yes. I see the Dutch children in uniform on the way to their schools. I've given the matter thought, and I feel it's best for my boys to attend school here, with the islanders."

Menno felt an instant connection with the doctor. Clearly, he had come to serve the local people — the mark of a true missionary.

The headmaster sat back in his chair and picked up his pipe. He patted down the tobacco, lit it and inhaled a few quick puffs. He fixed his gaze on his new friend. "Truthfully Doctor, how is the war effort progressing? I never quite trust the radio broadcasts. Sometimes the news reports seem overly optimistic. Could the war be over soon?"

Menno had heard the reports. Hitler's Wehrmacht had invaded the Netherlands on May 10, 1940, despite the Dutch government's decision to maintain neutrality. From her bunker in The Hague, Queen Wilhelmina had attempted to console the nation, but her swift escape to the United Kingdom with the royal treasury did little to allay the nation's fears. Many citizens felt abandoned and in despair. In London, Wilhelmina took charge of the exiled Dutch government.

Disquieting questions arose in Menno's mind. If conditions were worsening, how would their families in Holland fare under Nazi occupation?

The doctor looked down, thought a moment and pursed his lips. "I think we got out just in time."

3

HOME IS THE HEART

GOMBONG, CENTRAL JAVA, AUTUMN 1941

Menno and Flor's family had blossomed to seven vibrant, active children aged one to eleven years, and as usual, their chatter around the Giliam table had escalated to boisterous clamor. Due to the afternoon heat, school hours on the islands ran from seven o'clock in the morning until midday. Menno returned daily from the school to his home next door to join his wife and children at the table for the main family meal at noon.

Flor put her fork down and looked in earnest at Menno. He didn't seem to understand how difficult life in the Dutch Indies had been for her. While Menno had consistently remained optimistic, the oppressive heat and strange ways of their new culture had been very challenging for her.

Flor had made adjustments in an attempt to cope. First to go, were her European clothes. Not particularly suited for the climate and lifestyle, she replaced them with local batik sarongs for every day.

Next, she agreed to hire servants, albeit reluctantly. Nobody of their socio-economic status in Holland had domestic help, but it was an important gesture for Dutch missionaries in the Indies.

Hiring servants showed the locals that they supported them and welcomed them into their homes.

Kokkie [Cook] prepared the family's daily cuisine — always Indies food. Today it was *satay* — barbecued meat with peanut oil and soy sauce, *nasi goreng*, a family favorite that combined flavorful steamed rice, stir-fried eggs, and a choice of meat and vegetables. For dessert the children often enjoyed local sweets like rice or cassava cakes, but on this day, it was juicy, sweet mangos.

Dressed in her bright orange and rusty red sarong, *Kokkie* slipped quietly around the colonial harvest table removing the discarded mango peels. Flor patiently coached her three-year-old Ineke to finish eating the food on her plate. Menno, hunting for a passage to read at the end of the meal, carefully thumbed through a colorful, well-worn children's Bible.

Hilda suddenly lost patience with her wiry, older brother Pier. "Stop it! Stop kicking me! Papa! Pier is kicking me under the table!" She elbowed him, and he smiled mischievously.

Weary and annoyed, Menno peered through his reading glasses. "*Kinderen, maak niet zo veel herrie* [Children, don't make so much noise]!"

Flor could see from the children's behavior they craved their father's attention. She wished he could spend more time with them, but it didn't seem possible. In addition to his other responsibilities as headmaster, Menno taught school and marked papers late into the night. These tasks left him with little time for his own children.

"Papa. Why not come for a walk with us later when it's cool?" Flor implored, anticipating he would decline, yet she continued, "The children long to show you their garden."

"I'm sorry *schat*. Not today." Menno's thoughts were distant, his answer swift and final. "I need time to prepare for tomorrow's sermon."

Not all towns in the Dutch Indies had Protestant churches in the 1940s. The mission schools often also served as a local church, but without a pastor. Missionaries were duly called upon to pitch in wherever needed. Though not ordained, Menno was asked to "read" the prepared sermons written and mailed from the church head office in Holland. Being a teacher, he enjoyed adding some of his own commentaries to the readings, but it all took time. *Odd*, he thought, *this week's sermon hasn't arrived yet.* That left Menno with the added task of writing one himself.

Pier slurped his mango, casting a guilty, sidelong glance at his father. The children's bickering and misbehavior suddenly shattered Menno's thoughts, and he had had enough. His fist thundered down on the table sending the dinnerware clattering. *"HOU OP* [STOP]!"

Silence.

The children were shaken. They dared not move. Eyes cast downward, they carefully avoided their father's glare. A plaintive whimper sounded. Inconsolable, it quickly grew into an impassioned wail. Bawling Ineke trembled with fear.

Flor nodded to Yelly. Hot and exhausted, the mother of seven relied heavily on her eldest daughter's help with the children. Instinctively the eleven-year-old lifted her little sister gently onto her lap and attempted to calm her. The rest of the children sat silently around the table as the weeping abated.

Menno regained his composure and resumed his pursuit of the Scripture reading. "Uhh, hum. Let's see. Who remembers what we read yesterday?"

Hesitant silence.

"Certainly someone remembers!" Menno turned purposefully toward his namesake. "Menno? How about you?"

At an early age his blond, curly-haired son had shown an impressive aptitude for matters of faith and the Bible. "Joseph in the pit! Joseph in the pit!" enthused the six-year-old.

"Good, Menno. And who knows how he got there?"

Pier, eager to make amends, shot up his hand. "His brothers threw him in!"

Menno smiled. "Very good, children. You've remembered well. Now let's read ... "

A loud pounding at the door interrupted him. The children turned, curious to see who it might be. *Baboe* [maidservant] opened the door to a somewhat pudgy man in a white suit waiting, envelope in hand.

Menno pushed his chair from the table and went to his friend. *"Go'e dag Dominee Kijlstra* [G'day Reverend Kijlstra]. Won't you please come in? You're just in time for our Bible reading. Reverend, have you met our children?" With a sweep of his arm, Menno stepped aside to introduce his brood.

"Nay [No], I think not," replied the reverend, looking toward the table with interest.

The children sat still, quiet and obedient. Menno pointed out and introduced each one.

"Eleven-year-old Yelly is our eldest. Little Ineke on her lap is three. Next to me is Pier. He is ten. Hilda over here is eight. Then there's six-year-old Menno. That boy sure knows his Bible!"

"Maybe he will follow in his father's footsteps one day," the reverend chuckled, and Menno smiled.

He turned to his little, blonde daughter wearing a huge white bow. "And this," he grinned with pride, "is four-year-old Anneke."

"Six children!" the reverend marveled. "Quite some family you have."

"Actually, we have one more. Baby Jantine is sleeping in the crib," said Flor, joining her husband's side. "Please Reverend, stay for coffee after Menno reads to the children."

"Thank you *mevrouw*, but I must be making my way back to Keboemen. I just came to drop this off." He tossed a tattered envelope postmarked from the Netherlands on the table. "It's the sermon for tomorrow's church service. Just in time."

Flor rubbed her finger on the smudged postmark. "Oh, it's taken three months to arrive." Troubled, she mumbled, "The war is now affecting mail from Holland?" There always seemed to be a disruption to their family life.

The previous summer Flor had hoped to spend Menno's vacation together, but that had turned out to be a disappointment. Due to increasing concern over Japan's covert infiltration of the East Indies, and its growing aggression in Asia, Dutch male civilians of the East Indies had been called away for the entire month of July for military training. Menno returned home qualified as a KNIL military engineer reservist.

The reverend turned toward Menno who had accompanied him to the door. "We're so grateful you're able to lead the service on Sundays, knowing how busy you are with the schools."

"Just wait 'till I send you the bill," Menno chided, a twinkle in his eye.

Both men chuckled. Menno stepped out the door with the reverend and pulled him aside, careful not to be overheard. "Reverend, we're hearing the most disturbing rumors coming out of Europe. Is it really true — are the Jews of Germany now required to wear a yellow Star of David?" He found the thought particularly troubling.

Like most devout Protestant Christians, the Giliams were taught that the Jewish people are God's chosen ones and must be honored, even if it meant personal sacrifice. This biblical truth was such a vital part of their faith, that Menno later learned that his brother Jan Giliam, a detective in Haarlem, Holland, had been instrumental in saving numerous Jewish lives. Eventually, he had been betrayed and tortured by the Gestapo in February 1943.

"Yes. So I've heard," the reverend conceded. "We pray the war will be over soon."

"And if it isn't? What will happen to us? Who will fund the Dutch East Indies mission?"

Compassion filled the reverend's deep-set eyes. He clutched his friend's arm and entreated, "Menno, we must trust God."

≈

WITH CHRISTMAS 1941 FAST APPROACHING, FLOR AND HER BEST friend Mieke — a tall, slender Dutch woman with short, golden hair, set out for the local market. Hailing a small, three-wheeled pedicab, the two squeezed into the narrow back seat.

The Javanese driver pedaled casually through the streets maneuvering past hawkers, horse and buggies, and the occasional car. Just as they reached the street market, an elderly Chinese peddler, weighed down by a basket of squawking chickens, stepped in front of them. The driver stopped abruptly. "This is far enough," Flor uttered, leaning toward him to be heard over the noise.

Hiking up the hems of their sarongs, the women paid the driver and paused to inhale the welcoming aromas of local roasted delicacies. The driver, rewarded with a few coins, grinned broadly, revealing numerous missing teeth.

Bazooga! Bazooga! A shiny, black 30's convertible wove through the crowded street and stopped near the two women. An elegantly dressed politician's wife seated in the back next to her teenage daughter, a younger version of herself, waved and called, "Mieke! Mieke! Over here!"

With a clip in their step, Mieke and Flor walked to the automobile.

"Mieke, join me this afternoon for tea?" the woman asked.

"Certainly! I will look forward to that," replied Mieke. "But how are you, Corrie? Is your husband back from the capital?"

Flor stepped back and looked down.

"It's been lonely," sighed the woman with bored helplessness. "He's endlessly away in Jakarta busy stomping out the islanders' quest for power. Sukarno and his political friends, they're the problem, of course." She lifted a long-stemmed cigarette holder and lit a cigarette.

Albert, the cobbler, had been right about the islanders wanting independence. In 1927, the *Partai Nasional* Indonesia, headed by Sukarno, had caused an insurrection. Rival factions then followed, demanding social-religious reform. Fearing the influence of radical Muslim leaders, the Dutch started prohibiting them from making the yearly Hajj pilgrimage to Mecca. Now 1941, Menno's Dutch colleagues were warning him to be careful when travelling the countryside.

"I hear Sukarno is an eloquent orator," Mieke volunteered. "His followers are growing in number."

The politician's wife took a long puff of her cigarette and smirked. "With my husband in the capital, they don't stand a chance!"

"Mother, it smells here! I want to go home, *now*," complained the woman's daughter.

"*Nog een minutje, schatje* [Just one more minute, little darling]," crooned her mother. "As you can see, we must be on our way. Tea will be served at four o'clock!"

"*Tot ziens* [Good bye]!" Mieke replied and waved half-heartedly as the convertible lurched forward. She immediately turned to Flor.

"I am sorry, Flor." The upper crust of Dutch society welcomed Mieke, the wife of a Lieutenant into their social circles, but not missionaries.

Flor shrugged but remained silent as they strolled toward a colorful fabric stall.

Mieke thought a moment. "You know. I think ... she's jealous!"

"Jealous?" Flor glanced at Mieke disbelieving. "Of me?" They entered a crowded stall lined with hanging batik and colorful bolts of fabric. Flor thumbed through the stack near her.

Mieke seemed to be searching for the right words. "It's ... because ... well, look at you. You're young and lovely ... and ... you have a beautiful family!"

Her back toward Mieke, Flor didn't respond. She motioned to the aging Chinese merchant to unroll a bolt of red cotton.

Mieke kept pressing. "She just doesn't understand. Her kind are only interested in themselves and their fortunes. But you ... missionaries. You're ... different. You've come here to *help* the locals, not use them and take from them."

Flor's fingers scrutinized the red fabric and the price tag, but she heard.

"Besides," Mieke became mischievous, "you're not missing out. Those women can be *bo*-ring!" Flor glanced at her. Mieke mimicked the woman's hand movements holding an imaginary cigarette. "Let's see," she said sarcastically, "what shall I wear today? Mink or chinchilla?"

Flor smiled at her friend, understanding her good intentions, and conceded. Both women giggled.

With the tension lifting, Mieke became more animated. "Have you noticed how my Italian Damask drapes perfectly match my silk recliner? Humph!" she huffed. "Oh and yes! Don't ever, ever, *ever* expect me to eat *that*!" She pointed at a dusty sack of rice on the dirt floor of an adjacent stall. Dutch high society was known to prefer potatoes imported from Holland.

They cackled with laughter. Flor beckoned to the Chinese shop owner. Still giggling, she asked, *"Meneer, ik wil twee meter van deze rode stof, alstublieft* [Mister, I want three meters of this red fabric, please]." She turned to Mieke. "This is perfect for Christmas dresses for the girls. I think they'll love them."

The merchant handed Flor a package wrapped in newspaper in exchange for a wrinkled bill and her kind smile.

Leaving the stall, the women elbowed their way through the bustling alley. A loud, grinning street merchant raised his voice above the screeching of a chained monkey wrestling to break free. A greasy-haired hawker pushed past them pulling a rusty cart loaded with exotic local food. *"Lumpias! Saté! Bami!"* he hollered. *"Lumpias! Saté! Bami!"*

Slight uneasiness nagged at Flor. "They're friendly," she observed. "But you have to wonder what they're really thinking ... about us?"

"Yah," Mieke agreed, stopping at a busy intersection. "In their mind, this land is *their* home." Her gaze was distant. "One day we could wake up to discover we're no longer welcome here!"

4

THE COLOR RED

GOMBONG, CENTRAL JAVA, DECEMBER 1941

The clip-clop of horse's hooves approached the mission home, then receded. The soothing rhythm blended with the sound of Flor's black, gold-trimmed sewing machine as she bent over to stitch a child's cropped, red sleeve. Soon, a late afternoon breeze picked up, cooling the shaded *emper* (walkway) where she worked behind the house.

Hilda, Anneke and Ineke stood fidgeting by her side, clothed in unfinished red dresses. Each obediently stretched out an arm for Flor to measure. Yelly, seated in Flor's rattan chair, rocked sleeping Jantine in her arms.

Menno, preoccupied with his thoughts, entered the walkway carrying his military hard case.

"Papa! Papa! What's in there?" Little Menno eyed his father's luggage. He and Pier were sprawled on the grass behind the house, playing with their toy soldiers. Both quickly abandoned their make-believe battle scene and hovered around their father as he laid his case on the ground and cracked it open. Little Menno stared with amazement at the contents. "Are you going to kill Japs?" he asked, brimming with enthusiasm.

"Menno! Where did you hear such a thing?" Flor demanded, astonished at her gentle, young boy's words.

"Jantje's father told him he was going to kill Japs," Pier interjected.

Flor maintained her poise while exchanging distressed glances with Menno. He shook his head aggressively with implied distaste. "Oh no, no, *no*! Holland is at war, but here – no! *Jongen*, I am NOT going to 'kill Japs!'"

He diverted the boys' attention to the contents of the chest. "Look what I have here: a helmet, boots, a canteen. Wait. Where's my khaki shirt? *Baboe!* Please come!"

Immediately *Baboe* appeared in the doorway.

"Is my shirt still hanging to dry?"

"I will look, *Meneer* Giliam." She bowed her head respectfully and attended to her task.

Eager to play "real" soldiers, Pier begged his father, "Can I wear the helmet? Please, Papa? Please?"

Menno extracted his helmet and canteen from the chest.

"Okay, Pier. You wear this, and Menno, you take my canteen."

Menno Junior slung the canteen across his shoulder, while Pier donned the oversized helmet. His head disappeared into it, with the chin strap dangling. Proud to be wearing their father's military gear, the boys chased each other through the house shooting with loud, imaginary weapons.

"Bang! Bang! Kill a Jap! Kill a Jap!" Pier yelled.

"Pow! Pow!" retorted Menno.

From inside, the old, hand-carved clock chimed the hour prompting Menno to motion the family inside to the living room. He turned on his grand, upright mahogany radio — his pride and joy. They had saved a long time to buy it. Settling comfortably into a white rattan chair, he rested his head against the high back, shut his eyes and listened.

> *Daar boven juicht een grote schaar*
> *Van kindren voor God's troon*
> *Verlost van zonden van gevaar,*
> *Tot eer van's Vader's Zoon*

> [High in the sky is a tremendous throng
> Of children before God's throne
> Delivered from sin and danger,
> To the honor of the Father's Son]

How easily Menno could lose himself in the celestial sounds of the radio choir singing traditional Dutch hymns!

Outside, Flor placed a hand on her back and straightened to take a break from sewing. One by one, she slipped the half-finished dresses off the girls, helped them dress, and prodded them to join their father.

Across from Menno, Flor moved into her favorite chair, taking sleepy Jantine into her arms. The children, scattered on the tile floor, enthusiastically harmonized with the song:

> *Hoe kwamen ze in dat heerlijk oord?*
> *Zij hoorden Jezus' stem,*
> *Geloofden in Zijn dierbaar Woord,*
> *En gaven 't hart aan ...*

> How did they get to that lovely place?
> They heard Jesus' voice,
> Believing in His precious Word,
> And gave their heart to ...

Suddenly a news bulletin broke into the hymn. A radio announcer spoke in a monotone voice:

Early yesterday morning, the United States of America was deliberately attacked by naval and air forces of the Empire of Japan. The strike on Pearl Harbor has resulted in the loss of life estimated to number in the thousands.

The United States President Franklin Roosevelt is expected to announce US intentions to enter the war. The Dutch Allied Forces of the East Indies will likely follow.

The matter-of-fact voice continued:

In the coming days, all able-bodied Dutch male citizens of the colony could be called upon to serve their country.

"Lord! Help us!" Flor gasped, a wave of fear flooding her. She gaped wide-eyed at Menno, who, overcome with his thoughts, stared straight ahead then spoke, "I have much to get ready in the school."

Oblivious to the breaking news, *Baboe* returned and graciously presented Menno's military apparel, neatly folded. "*Meneer* Giliam, your shirt, sir."

$\sim$

ON DECEMBER 8, 1941, THE UNITED STATES DECLARED WAR ON Japan. Within four days the KNIL Royal Dutch Indies Army called up all able-bodied male Dutch expatriates for compulsory military duty.

The Governor General of the Dutch East Indies, Alidius Tjarda van Starkenborgh Stachouwer made the following statement to his compatriots:

… the Japanese Empire has consciously adopted a course of aggression. These attacks, which have thrown the United States of America and the British Empire into active war on the side of already-fighting China, have as their object the establishment of

42

Japanese supremacy in the whole of east and southeast Asia. These aggressions also menace the Netherlands East Indies in no small measure. The Netherlands government accepts the challenge and takes up arms against the Japanese empire.[1]

The Dutch Indies forces numbered about eighty-five thousand, with Dutch national troops forming the smallest group. The KNIL had about a thousand officers and thirty-four thousand enlisted men, of which twenty-eight thousand were indigenous to the islands. An additional five thousand Allied soldiers (American, British and Australian) would help defend against a Japanese invasion.

Holland's declaration of war against the Japanese was met with swift retaliation. The East Indies rubber plantations and oil wells were vital to Japan's war effort because the United States had halted all sales of natural resources to Japan.

With war upon them, and the Dutch men conscripted into the army, many families scrambled to escape the East Indies. For those who were unable to travel overseas, Bandung, a military stronghold, became the destination of refuge.

The Dutch populations suddenly in flux, large numbers of indigenous domestic helpers found themselves without work. Given no alternative, they were forced to return to their home villages, sometimes great distances away.

Soon Dutch Indies train stations became chaotic hubs of frantic travelers. At Gombong's small, one-room station a throbbing mass of loud, anxious passengers jostled to purchase what was left of the diminishing ticket supply.

Wealthy upper-class passengers, fearing robbery, gathered at the designated and guarded First Class waiting area just as the thunder of an approaching locomotive temporarily overpowered the din inside the station. With a piercing screech of wheels breaking against metal, and a loud hissing decompression of the steam engine, the train came to a stop.

A band of lean, dark-skinned island women dressed in colorful batik sarongs, stood by the tracks. Some carried their young in cloth slings on their backs.

The fumes of cigarette smoke drifted from a group of squatting men beside a haphazardly stacked tower of reed baskets and mingled with the savory aroma of roasted pork rising from a small fire fanned by a gray-haired vendor.

Passengers pushed to embark. The train doors slammed shut and the locomotive engaged. Three brazen youths leaped onto its side in an attempt to crawl through a remaining open window as the slow-moving train chugged out of the station.

Streetside of Gombong's station, a green military truck snaked its way through the swollen queue of travelers pressing to get in. The Dutch vehicle honked incessantly in its slow progress through the mob. Under the truck's swaying, khaki tarps rolled up above their heads, rows of glum Dutch soldiers, now in active duty, sat observing the tumult. Among them, Menno.

Not far from the train station, on the steamy tarmac of Gombong's Air Force base stood a well-dressed military wife wearing a fur-collared jacket. Despite the heat, she, like many women of her social status, was not prepared to part with her treasured items, even to save her life. Next to her stood her two blonde daughters in identical floral dresses with bows, and her tall, shrewd husband bearing the medals of a decorated Dutch air force officer.

She drew her daughters close as she glanced uncomfortably at her surroundings — the din of the military transport with its churning propellers and the workers on the field pushing a tall staircase toward its door. A sweaty soldier carried her weighty suitcases toward the plane.

The husband chuckled at his wife's efforts to grasp her elegant red hat and keep her matching skirt from flapping in the wind. They were indeed one of the privileged few families able to escape to Australia.

Ironically, as Dutch civilians with only a few month's training prepared to face the formidable Japanese war machine, numbers of Dutch government officials and military leaders seized the opportunity to take advantage of their positions to spirit their families and personal staff abroad quietly to safety.

~

BY JANUARY 1942, THE IMPERIAL ARMY HAD INVADED THE EAST Indies and had advanced rapidly, capturing the island of Java. Only two months since the Dutch Indies government had enforced conscription, the defending Allied Forces had suffered overwhelming losses. The European women and children left behind were consumed by their new reality — survival.

Flor and Mieke found support in each other. They sat relaxing in the back garden of the Giliam home on rattan outdoor chairs arranged under a shade tree. It was February 13, 1942 — two months since Menno had left for military duty. Flor wiped the sweat from her brow and gently rocked Jantine's carriage. The small child slept undisturbed despite the banter of the children playing in the nearby garden.

Sullied with dirt, the children scrupulously burrowed holes in the tropical soil. Bram and Inge, Mieke's blond-haired six and seven-year-olds, greatly enjoyed playing at the Giliam home.

The lieutenant's wife lifted a porcelain cup of sweet jasmine tea to her lips as Flor leaned forward and touched her lightly on the knee. "Mieke. You know you are always welcome to stay with us." Her voice was concerned yet gracious. "Inge can sleep in Hilda and Yelly's room, and Bram, on a mat with the boys. It'll be great fun for the children."

Mieke placed her cup on the saucer in her hand. "Thanks, Flor," she smiled, "that's very kind. But we'll be fine."

"*Mevrouw* Giliam! *Mevrouw* Giliam!" An ecstatic *Baboe* ran awkwardly toward Flor and Mieke waving her arms. The faithful servant arrived panting. "*Meneer* Giliam! He's home! He's home!"

Flor jumped to her feet, incredulous. "Menno is home?"

To her delight, Menno, dressed in his khaki uniform, emerged from the house through the shuttered doors beaming. He stopped momentarily, waved and strode toward them. The children bounded across the lawn crying, "Papa! Papa!"

Menno crouched to their height and held out his arms. "Papa's home, children! Papa's home!"

Flor hurried toward him with Mieke close behind. They watched as the children pounced gleefully, vying for his hugs and kisses. Menno stood, and extended a hand. "Mieke. Good to see you are well."

"Menno. We ... we ... were not expecting you! Today!" Mieke stumbled over her words.

Menno's gaze rested on Flor. He grabbed her hands and pulled them up as he drew her close.

"*Lieve schat* [Lovely darling]. It is so good to see you!" Flor blushed and reached up to stroke the stubble on his face. The younger children scurried around Menno, grabbing his pant legs, hungering for attention. She glanced at them and turned a smile toward her beloved husband. "We need to get you cleaned up!" she blustered happily.

"Flor ... " Menno said gently, holding her hands. He took a deep breath and looked regretfully into her eyes. "I won't be home long. I've only been given four days to sort out school matters. Then I'll need to return to duty."

Flor's face fell.

"We need to be brave, *mijn schat* [my darling]," he encouraged. "For all we know, the war will be over soon."

Though Menno held Flor protectively against his large physique, she found it hard to share her husband's optimism.

"Papa! Papa! Come see our tomato garden!" Young Menno grabbed his father's pant leg and pointed in the direction of the garden.

Menno lingered, his gaze penetrating deep into Flor's anxious eyes. Young Menno bounced around him until his father looked down at his little, eager dirt-streaked face. "Tomato garden? My, my! You children have been busy!"

"Wait!" Menno exclaimed. With a twinkle in his eye, he playfully patted several pockets pretending to search for something. "I almost forgot! Where ... where did I ... put ... "

"What is it, Papa?" cried Hilda, excited.

Yelly ventured, "Is it something for us?"

"Papa brought us something!" Pier shouted, jumping up and down as Menno slowly pulled a small, crude sackcloth pouch from a pant pocket. Breathless with anticipation, the children followed his every move as he loosened the string. He crouched down holding out the opened pouch. "Come, Yelly. You pick first. Inge and Bram, you come too. There is enough for everyone."

Taking turns, from oldest to youngest, each child picked out a brightly colored *knikkeren* game marble from the sackcloth.

"Marbles!" gaped Hilda, turning hers over in her hand and examining the miracle of the brilliantly blue glass ball.

The children quieted as they noticed Menno's silence and the kind, compassionate eyes. "Children," he addressed them, "I want you always to remember that just like each marble is special and different than the others, each one of you is very special to me, and to our heavenly Father."

He gazed intently from child to child. "Promise me, children, you will always remember this."

The children nodded solemnly clutching their precious glass balls in their little palms. Young Menno shut one eye, held up his blood-red stone and looked through it into the sun. "Everything is red!" he exclaimed in childlike wonder.

"Come, Papa! Come!" Hilda seized her father's hand. "Come see!"

Happy to oblige, Menno held her hand and set out for the back of the yard as the rest of the children skipped ahead, eager for him to see their workmanship.

~

Menno's few days at home passed quickly. Leaning back in his chair, he removed his heavy-rimmed glasses. He had worked long hours, yet there was still a mountain of manila files that needed his attention.

A knock sounded at the door of his school office. It opened cautiously to reveal *Baboe* and Flor carrying a freshly brewed pot of tea, a Delft blue porcelain cup, and warm, home-baked spice cake. Menno savored the pleasant aromas. "Ladies. Thank you. This will help keep me awake!"

Flor was concerned. "Menno, it's late. Won't you come home? The children are still waiting for you to read them their bedtime Bible story."

"Sorry, *schat,*" Menno looked regretfully at the files on his desk. "This all needs to be done before I leave tomorrow."

Despondent, Flor watched as *Baboe* carefully poured Menno's tea.

"*Dag,* Menno [Bye, Menno]. Please don't stay up too late," she begged as they turned to leave.

Already preoccupied with the work in front of him, Menno didn't look up. "Hmm … ja. *Dag, lieve schat* [… yes. Bye, darling]."

The women left the school in silence. Flor glanced once more at Menno's lone, softly illuminated figure visible in the night through his shuttered office window and walked swiftly back with *Baboe* to the mission home. Only the gurgling of frogs and trilling of crickets sounded in the night. The heavy, humid air on Gombong's main street was dark and ominously quiet.

～

EARLY MORNING RAIN PATTERED GENTLY ON THE TILE ROOF OF THE mission home. Flor sat at the large dining table trying to entice sixteen-month-old Jantine to eat. Near her, on the cool, ceramic floor, Anneke read her colorful picture book aloud while Ineke listened transfixed, hugging her favorite European doll.

Handsome, and neatly groomed in his pressed uniform, Menno strode into the room. Opening his hard case on the table, he removed two folders and tossed them toward Flor.

"Here's the last of the paperwork," he said, his mind still on school business. "A dozen more students approved, and as of today, all the local staff will get paid. Flor, can you make sure *Mevrouw* Kartono gets these?"

Menno unintentionally issued the command as if Flor was his secretary, yet she deferred to him. Tired and disappointed, she had hardly seen her husband during his few days at home.

The four oldest children, Yelly, Pier, Hilda and Menno, dressed for school, stood downcast and forlorn at the door. Menno, touched by his children's sadness, stepped toward them and crouched to their height. *"Jongens,"* he addressed his sons. "You'll take good care of Mama while I'm gone, won't you?"

The boys nodded neatly groomed blond heads. Little Menno stared at the floor pouting as his father hugged each sibling in turn.

Menno turned his gaze to Yelly and placed a gentle kiss on her cheek. *"And mijn flink Jeltje* [And my big girl Yelly]," he began. "You're always such a great help."

Resigned, Yelly nodded. Her curly, blonde waves, pulled into braids, revealed her sad face. She threw her arms around her father's neck and buried her face in his shoulder. He held his little girl tight.

Gently releasing her, he turned to his fourth oldest. "And here's Hilda. My sunshine!"

"Bye, Papa," she whispered.

Menno stroked Hilda's long, dark hair, then kissed her gently on the cheek.

The school bell chimed the start of classes, prompting Pier to step past his father. "Bye, Papa!" he said.

The others followed. *"Dag,* Papa! *Dag* [Bye, Father! Bye]!"

Menno watched the children run through the rain to the school. His gaze lingered until they were out of sight.

"Oh! I almost forgot!" Menno snapped out of his reflection to pull folded papers from his chest pocket. "Flor. Please see that these sermon notes get to Reverend Kijlstra. He'll need someone to replace me."

Two loud honks sounded down the street signaling the approach of the military transport vehicle.

"They're already here?" Menno glanced at the clock, startled.

The green army lorry, carrying a dozen soldiers, splashed through a puddle and halted by the front gate.

"Oh, Menno ... " Flor stood to her feet holding Jantine. Their time together was over far too quickly. "I will miss you." Tears glistened in her eyes.

Menno reached out his hand to her. *"Schat,* I have to go," he said, pulling her close for a gentle kiss before bending down to rub Jantine's soft wavy hair.

Military case in hand, Menno stepped out the door. Flor followed to the threshold. Silent and troubled, she bobbed Jantine on her hip. Anneke and Ineke trailed behind, oblivious to the gravity of the moment, and the image of their father that would fade over time.

On the porch, Menno turned to face Flor one last time. Teary and unable to hide her anxiety, she reached to touch his cheek. "Promise me — you'll write?"

Menno leaned his face into her hand. Struggling with his own fears and emotions, he gazed deep into her eyes. "I promise."

The impatient driver revved his engine.

"Bye, my little ones," Menno whispered to Anneke and Ineke. He bent to kiss them. As he straightened, Flor leaned forward to give him one last peck on the cheek.

Agitated, the driver began rolling the vehicle forward as the tropical rain increased. Menno ran to the lorry, tossed in his hard case and leapt into the open carriage. His curls, wet with rain, shed droplets down his face. He squinted for one last glimpse of Flor and waved as the tarp unfurled and dropped. The lorry disappeared down the street and into the storm.

Flor's heart was heavy. Tears clouded her vision. As quickly as Menno had appeared, he was now gone. Flor had no choice. She would face the uncertainty of the days ahead — alone.

---

1. *The Kingdom of the Netherlands Declares War with Japan.* Inter-Allied Review, December 15, 1941. Link: ibiblio.org/pha/policy/1941/411208c.html

PHOTOS

*Menno and Florence Giliam's Wedding Photo, Friesland,
Holland, Sept. 3, 1928.*

Dutch Indies Christian School, Gombong, staff and children. Far left is the Giliam Mission Home. [1]

Menno Giliam with teaching staff in Keboemen 1931. [1]

Menno and Florence Giliam, new missionaries. 1929.

Florence Giliam in Dutch Indies clothing, 1929.

Menno Giliam with students in Wonosobo, 1938.

40 year celebration of Queen Wilhelmina's reign, Sept. 6, 1938. From right, first child: Jelly (pronounced Yelly), third: Pier, sixth: Hilda Giliam.

5

CUT OFF

Gombong, Central Java, March 1942

Disorderly islanders and Dutch expatriates crammed into the simple one-room post office to escape the tropical mid-day shower. Flor, with sleeping Jantine in a cloth sling on her back, stood anxiously at the front of the pushy mob eager to be served. Behind the wooden counter a saronged Indies clerk with greased-back dark hair and rimmed glasses glanced up. "Next!" he called, stressed by the tension, but choosing to remain cordial.

Flor nodded and approached the wicket. *"Dag Meneer* [Good day, Sir]. This letter needs to go to Keboemen." She pushed a white envelope toward the clerk who pasted a stamp on it bearing Queen Wilhelmina's profile.

"Ah … let me see. Ah … yes," said the clerk, taking his time as he studied the address. "Reverend Kijlstra in Keboemen. Yes. The postage is correct."

"And one more thing. Please check if there is any mail for me — uh, for *Meneer* Menno Giliam, that is."

The clerk studied the row of alphabetized wooden pigeonholes on the wall behind him. "G ... G ... G ... Giliam. *Meneer* Menno. Yes! Here you are, *mevrouw*."

"Thank you! *Goedemiddag* [Good day]!"

"*Alstublieft, mevrouw* [You're welcome, Madam]. Next!"

Flor read the return address on the envelope and smiled. Ducking through the mob of post office customers, she hurried back to Mieke, Anneke and Ineke, who were waiting inside the entrance. The girls leaped to greet their mother. Mieke glanced through the open door and commented, "Looks like the rain has stopped. Did you get everything you need?"

Flor waved the letter from the church head office and smiled, "Got it!"

The women hustled the children out the door into the busy street. Dozing Jantine rode contently on her mother's back while the two girls skipped along at Flor's side unaffected by the throng streaming by with bags, suitcases, and children in tow. The multitude on foot, and the traffic of automobiles, all moved in the same direction — out of town.

Flor carefully tore open the letter and pulled out a gold-trimmed Dutch bank check. She clutched it against her chest, inhaled and smiled. "Thank you, Lord!"

Accompanying the check was an official red-slugged letter from the Christian mission head office dated March 1, 1942. Flor began reading but stopped abruptly. Her face crumbled.

"This must be a mistake!" Had she misunderstood? Holding the letter with both hands, she re-read it under her breath: " ... and due to unforeseen circumstances, we regret to inform you that the Dutch Indies mission will no longer fund ... " Flor looked at Mieke stunned.

"Flor, what's the matter?"

"This is it! The last one!" Flor held up the check.

Mieke shook her head in disbelief. "Good Lord! They can't be serious!"

The honking of a 1930s black sedan steering toward the women sent them hustling to the side of the road with their children. From the driver's seat, the familiar face of Dr. de Jong beamed. *"Mevrouw* van Dijk! *Mevrouw* Giliam!" he hollered through the open window and stopped near the women.

"Doctor! You're still here!" Flor was both surprised and relieved.

"Yah!" he said, as he jumped from the car. "Physicians and clergy are exempt from military service — for now. But let's see how long that lasts!" His brow wrinkled as he leaned in to look more closely at the women. "How are you both holding up?"

His gaze intensified. "Flor, you look troubled."

She lifted the check for him to see. "This is our last one, Doctor. We've been cut off!"

"Yes. I know," he sighed. "All of us serving with the Indies mission won't be getting any more checks."

Mieke was flabbergasted. "What in heaven's name are you going to do?"

The doctor, calm yet firm, looked intently at the ladies. "Take my advice. Don't wait too long to withdraw your funds," he warned. "If the situation worsens, the banks may decide to freeze your accounts."

"How do they expect us to survive?" Flor gasped.

"Yah ... now," the doctor shook his head. "We're all trying to figure that out. See those people?" The muddy rain-drenched road in front of them was bustling with activity: a flustered owner of an expensive, black sedan, carrying mahogany furniture strapped to the roof, yelled at a stopped pedicab driver haggling with a young Dutch woman. A horse-drawn buggy splashed past a hunched, elderly Dutchman struggling to carry a worn case as groups of locals in traditional outfits shouldering heavy rattan baskets trudged by.

"They're on their way to Bandung," said the doctor.

Anneke, growing impatient, tugged on her mother's sleeve. "Mama. Can we go home?"

Ineke, beside her, looked eagerly at Flor. "Go home?"

Flor drew her daughters close, kissing Anneke on the head. "We'll go soon."

"The Japs are moving fast," he continued. "I reckon it's a matter of days, maybe less, before they get here. But Bandung is still heavily fortified with Dutch troops."

The doctor pointed again at the parade of travelers. "They are all convinced it's safer there."

He glanced at his watch and reached for his car door. "Now, if you'll excuse me, I must get to the hospital. It was good to see you, ladies."

"But wait, Doctor!" Flor called after him, taking a step toward the car. "What do you suggest we do?"

"Should we try to get to Bandung, too?" Mieke asked.

Taking a deep breath, the doctor paused and looked at the women. Then he continued to get into his car. Flor and Mieke came to the door. He revved the engine a few times, leaned an elbow out the window and looked at them. "Only God knows," he shrugged.

Flor felt lost, afraid and vulnerable. With military clashes imminent, it was now solely up to her to make all the critical decisions for the survival of her young family.

As the doctor maneuvered his vehicle into the crowded street, little Jantine stirred. Flor and Mieke stood stunned. They had not gained much comfort from their conversation with the physician. "I wish Menno were here," Flor pined. "He would know what to do!"

~

LATER THAT EVENING, FLOR LEANED AGAINST THE NEATLY PRESSED linen pillows of her white, wrought-iron poster bed. Delicate, white mosquito nets draped casually against the bed poles. Her hair pulled back into a loose bun, she held Ineke on her lap while her three oldest girls, in embroidered cotton nightdresses, cuddled around her. Pier and Menno sprawled on their stomachs at the end of the bed, the younger, reading carefully, sounding out the words from the family's colorful children's Bible. The others listened to the story, as was their bedtime custom.

" ... So five th-ow ... th-ow-sand ... men sat down. Jesus took the five low-ves ... and two fish from the small boy gave thanks and then gave the pea-poll ... as much as they wanted. Then e-ver-ee ... , e-ver-ee-one ... had enough to eat!"

"Dolly is hungry! She can eat!" chimed Ineke. She danced her doll on the bedspread making the others laugh.

"Very good reading, Menno." Flor praised her son. "Amazing, heh? From only five loaves of bread and two fish, so many people ate!"

Excited, Yelly exclaimed, "It was a miracle!"

"Mewr-ak-o! Mewr-ak-o!" Ineke parroted, absorbed in her play.

The children giggled, but Flor was deep in thought. Their lives were in danger and she desperately needed guidance. The children must know about their situation, but how would she tell them?

She and Mieke had both been invited to join a special convoy of officer's wives heading to the fortified town of Bandung, but Flor was unsure. What would she and seven children do there?

Mieke was considering the move, and Flor urged her not to be influenced by her choice. Ultimately both women decided to commit the question to God in prayer and ask for His leading before making a decision.

Flor waited for the children to quiet down. Then she spoke. "Children, you know that Jesus' miracles are for us today, just as they were for the people in the Bible."

The children listened earnestly to their mother and nodded.

"Well. We need to ask our Heavenly Father for a miracle." Her voice quivered. "The mission can no longer send us money ... and ... "

The children watched her trustingly.

" ... and ... many, many families are going to Bandung. They think it is safer there. Children, we need to ask Jesus if we are to go to Bandung, or if we're to stay here."

"We pray Mama!" announced Menno.

As Flor and the children slipped from the bed onto the floor to kneel, the shouting of defiant male islanders erupted on the street outside the house. Angry mobs of nationalists had already ransacked some of the homes in Gombong. Were they now on Flor's street?

With the Dutch forces preoccupied with Japan and the Dutch colonial police force crumbling, rebels had seized the opportunity to free themselves from Dutch imperialism. Called *rampassers*, or looters, they ran barefoot through the streets in gangs yelling obscenities, ransacking homes, and raping and murdering their occupants. They were determined to take vengeance on the remnant of Dutch "oppressors" be they women and children, the infirm and the elderly. Clearly, the highly disciplined Japanese fighters who were conquering the island at an alarming pace were not their only danger.

"Mama!" The sound of angry voices frightened Anneke, and she wrapped her arms around Flor's neck. The other children looked apprehensively toward their mother but followed her lead to pray. Together they knelt, hands folded, eyes closed, along the three sides of the poster bed.

"Our Father in Heaven, who watches over us and keeps us, please help us ... " Flor's voice cracked. She sniffled and struggled to continue. "Father please show us what to do and provide for us. We really need you. In Jesus name. Amen."

Flor opened her eyes to observe the children in deep and sincere prayer. Heads pressed against tiny folded hands, they were oblivious to her anguish. Such pure and unfettered faith ...

... and then something unexpected happened.

A calming peace quieted her soul and melted away the tension of worry. Flor recited Psalm 91 to them. It was Scripture she knew well.

> *He who dwells in the shelter of the Most High*
> *will abide in the shadow of the Almighty.*
> *I will say to the Lord, My refuge and my fortress,*
> *my God, in whom I trust.*
>
> *... Because you have made the Lord your dwelling place*
> *—the Most High, who is ... [your] ... refuge—*
> *no evil shall be allowed to befall you,*
> *no plague come near your tent.*
> *For he will command his angels concerning you*
> *to guard you in all your ways.*

The words seemed to be just for Flor. Peace settled in her heart and she was certain God would keep His promises to them.

6

THE INDIES ARE FALLING

GOMBONG, CENTRAL JAVA, MARCH 1942

The following afternoon a Chinese businessman showed up at Flor's doorstep. She wasted no time directing him to the wooden furniture in her sitting room. Whether Flor decided to stay or go to Bandung, she had another immediate need — money. For that she had devised a plan: sell all unnecessary furniture to the local wealthy Chinese.

The stern-faced man in a three-piece suit rubbed his goatee as he scrutinized a handcrafted Chinese cabinet. Flor held Jantine on her hip while he pondered his response.

"How much?" he demanded abruptly in a broken Chinese-Indies accent.

"One hundred guilders."

"Whaaaat? One hundred guilders? Nay *mevrouw*. That is too much!"

Flor's heart sank. How she hated to lose the sale! With furrowed brow she watched the outraged Chinese businessman dart out of her house. He stormed past two young Dutch teachers dressed in army uniforms approaching the entrance of the mission home.

Flor knew them well. Both had taught at Menno's schools.

"Mevrouw Giliam," the shorter of the two greeted her and cocked his head in the direction of the Chinese businessman. "Someone's in a hurry."

Jantine still in her arms, Flor walked to the door to greet them. "Wim and Pieter! What a surprise to see you! Looks like my husband's teaching staff are getting ready to go to war."

Tall, lanky Pieter exclaimed, *"Mevrouw* Giliam! Good to see you."

"Please come in. Can you stay for coffee?"

Wim glanced questioningly at his comrade. "We really can't stay long. The transport will be leaving soon. We're on our way to Bandung."

"Kokkie, please pour some coffee," Flor called to the kitchen. "Gentlemen, do come in for a few minutes."

"Mevrouw, how are you coping with *Meneer* Giliam's absence?" asked Wim as he and Pieter followed Flor into the sitting room.

"Managing." Flor pursed her lips and shrugged as she motioned for her guests to sit down.

"We're relieved to see you're still here," said Pieter. "With so many leaving for Bandung, that is *not* the place you want to go."

"Really?" Flor stared at them, alert and listening. "Why?"

"Mevrouw Giliam, it's unsafe to travel the roads. *Rampassers* are everywhere. We also told our wives to stay home."

"With so many trying to find refuge," added Wim, "Bandung could soon be closed to civilians."

"Gentlemen, you have no idea how I needed to hear this."

The wall clock chimed the hour. *"Kerel* [Man]! Look at the time!" Wim jumped up and turned to his colleague. "We need to catch the army transport, or *we'll* be walking with the bandits!"

"Please, *mevrouw,*" said Pieter, rising from his chair, "pay attention to the radio. The situation is changing by the minute."

Flor thanked the teachers and accompanied them to the door. They shook her hand respectfully and disappeared into the endless horde of refugees parading past her home.

Greatly relieved, Flor returned to the sitting room to catch the morning newscast. She placed Jantine on the floor beside her, switched on the radio, and sat down on the cushioned rattan chair.

"Mevrouw, here is *Koffee."* *Kokkie* appeared with steaming fresh brew.

"O Sorry! The teachers had to leave suddenly. They are already on their way."

The gentle servant smiled knowingly before she placed the coffee for Flor on the table, bowed graciously, then turned to leave.

"Thank you." Flor's heart filled with gratitude as she savored the tasty brew and the moment. God had clearly answered their prayers. Traveling to Bandung was far too dangerous.

With renewed purpose, Flor listened to the radio.

From the mahogany box the noise of shuffling papers transmitted through the broadcast. A baritone announcer's voice then followed. "The mayor has just arrived to make an important public announcement."

"Citizens of Gombong, I regret to inform you, the war is quickly escalating. Many Dutch soldiers are now captured. Exact numbers still to be determined."

"Dear Lord!" It was not the news she had expected. The mayor continued:

"Japanese troops are advancing and are expected to arrive in Gombong before noon. All citizens are to remain indoors and out of view as gunfire with incoming Australian Allied Forces will likely ensue. I repeat: All citizens are to remain indoors ... "

The mayor continued, but Flor had heard enough. The mission home, situated on Gombong's main thoroughfare, lay directly on the route of the advancing Japanese army. Mieke, aware of the potential danger, had decided to stay in her own home located on a nearby side street.

Flor leapt from her seat. *"Baboe!* Come! Watch Jantine and the girls. I must get the children from school!"

On the street outside, colorful wooden shutters clattered shut as people hastily prepared for the approaching armies. Frantic locals darted about to find shelter. A Dutch military vehicle zoomed past as a squawking chicken attempted to fly out of its way.

With the low rumble of battle already sounding in the distance, Flor, breathing hard, rushed to the school next door. War was at the door!

SURABAYA, EAST JAVA, MARCH 1942

The back neck flaps of the Japanese sergeant's straight-rimmed khaki cap tussled in the warm afternoon breeze. Distinguished by the large sword that hung from a leather scabbard at his side, the firebrand disciplinarian studied the newly captured Dutch fighters with a sadistic glint in his eyes. Expressionless Japanese soldiers, rifles ready, flanked the sergeant, anticipating his every move.

Only three months after the official declaration of war on Japan, dozens of sullied and exhausted KNIL soldiers paraded through the gates of what was formerly a Dutch Indies military base in Surabaya, Java.

The Imperial Army had moved swiftly in its campaign to occupy the Dutch Indies. By targeting strategic seaports on the island of Java, they had successfully captured Tanjung Priok and Surabaya in the north, and on the south coast, Tjilatjap — the only port left that could have handled large ships.

On March 8, 1942, the Allied Forces had surrendered to the Japanese. Dread clouded the minds of the captured soldiers who now lived at the mercy of their notoriously brutal Japanese captors.

Behind the troops entering the military base, limped bloodied and wounded civilian recruits struggling to understand the steely Japanese barking incomprehensible commands. Rifles cocked and loaded, they herded the band of POWs into an enclosure just beyond the barracks.

Once on the grounds, Menno dropped his muddied case and cumbersome military duffle. Though bone-weary, he projected an air of defiance. He felt incapable of accepting defeat at the hands of a fighting force half his stature.

"Kio'tsuke!" Came the sergeant's command.

Bewildered, the Dutch looked at each other.

The sergeant screamed louder, *"KIO'TSUKE!"*

A Japanese soldier by the sergeant's side motioned for the men to stand at attention, and slowly the POWs grasped the command. One by one they straightened and stood in lines.

"Rei!" the sergeant bellowed.

Still standing at attention, but uncertain, the POWs glanced around. One soldier bowed. The rest complied, bending in submission. The sergeant's "assistants" followed, counting the men in their awkward position. Menno fixed his gaze ahead as the military exercise played out around him. He refused to participate.

With a critical eye, the sergeant scanned the field of Dutch POWs. His face flushed and his nostrils flared. He marched straight to Menno, his spurred leather riding boots clicking with each step. Mere inches from the headstrong Frisian's chest he barked the order directly into his face, "*REI* [BOW]!"

Unflinching, Menno continued to ignore the command.

The outcome was swift and merciless. Four mighty blows to Menno's skull sent crushing pain through his temples and jaw. His vision disappeared. The world spun. As he crumpled, a final blow to the gut sent him sprawling in the dirt. Writhing in pain, he cushioned his bleeding head with both hands.

The disciplinarian lit a cigarette and waited. Taking a few quick puffs, he looked down at Menno on the ground groaning and clutching his stomach. Blood stained the dirt around him.

The two Japanese soldiers nodded to each other and signaled the counting was complete. The sergeant dropped what was left of his cigarette and crushed it under his boot.

"*Naorei* [Stand erect]!" came the command.

The POWs cautiously straightened.

"*Sagarei* [Dismissed]!"

Chaotic yelling ensued. Waving their rifles, the Japanese soldiers motioned for the POWs to gather their belongings and continue toward the white-walled, Dutch-style military barracks.

Menno couldn't move.

"*Ben je helemaal gek geworden* [Have you completely lost your mind]?"

His tall and good-natured friend Willem de Graaf hovered over him in disbelief. Next to him, shaking his head, stood another one of his trusted companions, Hans de Wit. Menno half-opened his eyes and looked at his friends as they pulled him up. "Don't think ... uhhhh ... ouch ... I'll do that again." He groaned as he limped to the barracks, leaning on their shoulders.

~

JAPANESE AND AUSTRALIAN MILITARY CONVOYS WERE RAPIDLY closing in on the mission home. The family could hear them approach from opposite directions, heading toward the town's main intersection — in front of the house.

With only precious seconds remaining before the troops appeared, Flor hastily gathered her children by the door of the musty underground shelter along the side of the house. Jantine propped on one hip, she waited as anxious seconds ticked by while *Kokkie* forced the rusty latch to open. It gave way, and together *Kokkie* and Flor heaved open the heavy, weathered wood door. "Children! Come quickly!" Flor urged.

The girls descended into the shelter just as Japanese military vehicles pulled up almost directly in front of their house.

At the same time Aussie troops assigned to slow Japanese progress arrived to intercept them.

The Japanese soldiers jumped out, ran through the gate across the lawn to the hedge just a few meters from the shelter and positioned themselves to fire at the approaching Australians.

Green, khaki-clad Aussies with side-flapped canvas caps, shorts and stockinged legs, leapt from the Australian convoy. A stout sergeant yelled for the men to take cover behind the white stucco fence.

At that moment *Kokkie* entered the shelter behind the girls.

Flor, about to follow, suddenly realized that some of her children were missing. She panicked. "Where are the boys? And where is *Baboe*? They must be at the front of the house." She dashed back and spotted Pier and Menno crouched behind the balcony railing on the front porch peeking curiously through the floral-patterned holes, fascinated by the Australian soldiers positioning for action.

"Pier! Menno! In the shelter! Now!" Flor grabbed the boys by the hand and dragged them to the side of the house. Struggling with the latch, she pleaded, "Come ... on! Open ... pleeease!"

The rumble of a Japanese reinforcement motorcade intensified amidst the clamor of the Aussies.

"More Japs are here!" Menno shouted with excitement.

Desperate, Flor yanked on the door as Japanese soldiers emerged from their vehicles barking commands.

Suddenly *Baboe* was at Flor's side. As she grabbed the latch to help pry it open, it gave way. The two women flung the door back on its hinges with a loud thud. "Menno! Pier! Get in!"

The boys, followed by Flor, scrambled into the shelter. *Baboe,* right behind them, slammed the door shut. She had barely set foot on the shelter floor when loud cracks of gunfire exploded at the front of the house. *Kokkie* adjusted the wick of a flickering oil lamp to light the cramped quarters of the tiny room, a meter wider than a bed. "It stinks in here Mama!" said Hilda. In the hot, stagnant air the cramped space smelled earthy and humid.

Seated on wooden crates on the dirt floor, the girls gazed searchingly at their mother. Yelly gently stroked frightened Ineke, who cuddled against her. Still mesmerized by the soldiers, Pier and Menno whispered excitedly to each other.

Flor collapsed onto an overturned box next to the children. Behind her, the shelter doubled as storage with shelves that held jars along the walls. On the floor, scattered about, were large bottles of pickled roots.

Outside the gunfire escalated. Muffled Japanese voices yelled above the continuous, strident cracking and hissing of rifle fire.

Pier, absorbed in the dramatic events, re-enacted an imagined scene. "Australians are behind the fence! Japs in front! Pow! Pow! They're shooting Japs," he narrated to no one in particular.

"Ugh," Flor sighed, holding her head wearily, "Pier, please!"

"Mama," Hilda whined.

"Yes, *schatje?*"

"I don't feel so good."

Flor's hands dropped. She stared at Hilda. Pale and unhappy, Hilda sat rubbing her stomach.

"Oh, *lieve schat!* I know. It's your nerves."

"No, Mama. I have to go to the toilet!"

Flor stared at Hilda another moment and directed her to a small potty she had brought with her.

Hilda had diarrhea. The potty quickly filled leaving a nauseating stench amplified by the extreme heat and humidity.

Before long, Hilda had to go again. There was only one option. Flor jolted to her feet, grabbed Hilda's hand, lifting her, and turned to *Baboe* and *Kokkie*. "Help me get the door open! I have to take Hilda to the house!"

"No, *mevrouw!*" *Baboe* objected. "The fighting! It's too dangerous!"

"We have no choice," Flor retorted.

With *Baboe's* help, she heaved open the shelter door, helped Hilda out and emerged behind her. Acutely aware of how visible they were to the Japanese soldiers, she marched calmly with Hilda, head down, alongside the house to the kitchen door.

As Flor turned the door handle, she glanced at the battle. The Japanese fired at the Aussies as they crouched behind their vehicles. Bullets ricocheted, and one soldier lay on her front lawn. Dead! Flor looked away quickly and hurried Hilda through the door.

Inside the shelter, *Kokkie* held up the oil lamp. In the soft light, she saw compassion for the children stir *Baboe*. The servant's eyes filled with tears at their innocent, trusting faces against the backdrop of the battle raging outside. Minutes crawled by in Flor's absence.

The kitchen door swung open just as another Japanese soldier fell. Flor emerged calm and purposeful, Hilda in hand. She walked swiftly back to the shelter door. This time it opened with ease.

Exclamations of relief greeted them. Flor joined her children, her arm around Hilda. Before long the gunshots dwindled in frequency and abated.

"Mama, is it over?" Yelly asked.

"Can we go out?" queried Pier, eager to explore.

"Maybe *schat*," Flor responded cautiously and rose to her feet. She pushed the cellar door open a crack. A warm, gentle gust of air brushed her face, yet the putrid odors of gunfire and wounded flesh lingered.

Baboe and *Kokkie* emerged first, hesitantly. Then the girls. Ineke steadied herself, holding Yelly's hand as she climbed out. Pier and Menno, next, sobered quickly at the scene before them. The white fence was riddled with bullet holes and sprayed with blood. Large bullet casings lay everywhere, and the grass where the injured and dead had fallen appeared dark and wet.

Flor climbed out last. Strands of hair lay softly against her cheeks and the formal, tightly pulled bun had loosened giving her a casual beauty. Her eyes, resolute and strong, took in the battle scene.

Gently yet firmly she coaxed her little ones. "Come children. You too, *Kokkie* and *Baboe*. Let's go into the house and thank the Lord."

The full magnitude of what had taken place on the street outside the mission home that day became clearer in the days that followed.

Gombong had fallen into the hands of the Japanese.

FLOR, I LOVE YOU

SURABAYA POW INTERNMENT CAMP, 1942

Menno learned quickly to cherish every stolen moment of solitude. The POWs worked long hours under the glare of angry Japanese eyes and relentless aggression. Many cleaned and repaired the harbor, which the Japanese had bombed. Some labored in military facilities and others in manufacturing plants, like the factory that made peanut butter where Menno worked.

It was the end of a busy workday and Menno, pensive, leaned against the fluted base of a tropical Indies tree. He knew POWs were forbidden to write letters, let alone mail them, but writing to Flor gave him time to reflect on his experiences and address his deepest yearnings. Most of all, the tiny notes to Flor on scraps of paper gave him a sense of her closeness.

Beside Menno, the remaining delicate white flowers of a once manicured bush fluttered carelessly in the warm, late-afternoon breeze. Shutting his eyes, he inhaled their gentle scent. In the Indies the tiny white blossoms often adorned brides, and their sweet fragrance carried Menno's thoughts to his lovely Flor. It was risky to write, but he had to.

～

DECEMBER 5, 1942

Dear Flor,

Lately, I often think of writing you a letter. I know that you will not receive it personally right away. In all probability, I will, in fact, be the deliverer. Nevertheless, I continue to write, because I need to be able to concentrate on you this way.

I especially need to tell you how much I love you. Flor, you are so precious to me. And my children are so dear to me also. So much has happened, I will try to explain.

What you need to know is that you will find me a changed man. Of all the POWs captured by the Japanese here on the island of Java, not many still think as they did before March 8, 1942. I have changed in that my love for you, for my little children and especially for my Heavenly Father has become much more real to me. Flor, you know that there was love before, but it has now become immensely richer.

～

IN TINY LETTERS, HE WROTE ALONG THE FINE RED LINES. THE SUDDEN sound of advancing, measured strides arrested him. Menno stuffed the incomplete note into his canteen. Seconds later the steps came to a halt beside him.

"Oh, good! It's only you," Menno breathed, relieved to see it was his good friend de Graaf, not a prying Japanese guard. He retrieved his unfinished letter from its hiding place.

"Thought I'd find you here," de Graaf grinned and cocked his head sideways for a glimpse. His expression changed. He pursed his lips in sincere disapproval.

"You know, you're tinkering with your life," he said, pointing to the note. "If the Japs catch you writing about this hell hole, they'll kill you."

"Graaf, if I am going to get out of here — alive, I need to keep thinking about Flor and the children."

Though de Graaf shook his head in disapproval, a subtle grin betrayed his amusement. "Clearly, nothing's gonna change your mind. But I gotta say, Menno, sometimes you worry me."

❧

LAW AND ORDER IN THE COLONY DISSOLVED AS GOVERNANCE SHIFTED from Dutch to Japanese rule. In the wake of the Gombong battle, the Imperial army left a trail of anarchy in their advance across the island toward the southern harbor of Tjilatjap. Their arrival at Nusa-Kebangan maximum security prison sent the prison staff into disarray. The guards rioted and the prisoners escaped.

Consequently, large numbers of dangerous criminals were now on the loose among the *rampassers*, terrorizing communities on the Great Post Road, and making travel from Gombong to Bandung even more dangerous. The local police no longer provided protection, the few remaining Dutch troops were fighting skirmishes with the invaders, and the Japanese had not yet imposed order. Fear gripped the Dutch colonialists who remained in their homes along the formerly quiet, tree-lined streets of Gombong. Many suffered emotional breakdowns, or came close to it, under the unrelenting pressure.

Flor grew increasingly vigilant trying to protect the children, her home and servants. With school cancelled, her four oldest remained at home with the little ones. Flor insisted they stay inside.

After a Dutch neighbor, who lived alone, was murdered, the constant threat of terror instilled fear, especially in the children. Flor felt compelled to watch at her window and monitor the situation on her own street.

Through the narrow slits between the wooden shutters, Flor could see the house of the European family across the street. A

Dutch woman named Corrie lived there with two young boys and a German Shepherd. Her husband, a military officer, had been called into service.

One day Flor noticed Corrie stumble out her front door, one hand on the door frame, the other against her head. With a few faltering, running steps she arrived in the middle of the street pacing and moaning, "Oh ... oh ... oh. *Wij gaan allemaal sterven! Allemaal dood* [We are all going to die! Everyone dead]! Oh ... oh ... oh! They are going to kill us! We're all going to die!"

Her aging dog paced by her side, while her boys stood confused and wailing at the door of her house.

At the same time, a gang of Indies looters down the road were quickly advancing toward the mission home.

Hilda stood watching with Flor. The woman's distressed behavior shocked them. "Moma!" cried Hilda in alarm, drawing close to her, tears glistening in her eyes.

"*Schat,* I must go to help her!" Flor gently released Hilda, bolted to the front door and stepped outside.

"Corrie! Come here!" She motioned frantically to her neighbor hoping not to attract the attention of the approaching vandals.

Disoriented and traumatized, Corrie continued pacing, mumbling, moaning, "*Allemaal sterven. Allemaal dood. Allemaal sterven. Allemaal dood* [We're all going to die. Everyone dead. We're all going to die. Everyone dead]. Oh ... oh ... oh! Ohhhhh!"

Flor could see that her neighbor's nerves had unraveled at the stress of recent events, and she was unable to take in the offer of help.

There wasn't much time. Flor glanced down the street and decided to take a chance. The noisy gang was still a distance away, but they had already spotted the distressed woman on the street. Flor ran over to her house, took the boys by their hands and led them down the stairs to their mother. She lovingly wrapped an arm around her. "Come, Corrie! Come home with me. It's safer inside."

The boys clung to the skirt of their mother, who leaned heavily on Flor. The tiny group made their way back to the house.

"Flor!" a strained voice called from behind. It was Mieke, with Inge and Bram each hauling a heavy suitcase. Sweaty and out of breath, Mieke continued, "We're ... huh ... huh; taking up ... huh ... huh; your offer to stay with you!"

Mieke's hand shook as she pointed to the west. Flor squinted against the setting sun. In the distance another unruly gang was bearing down on them. Like wild dogs they moved in packs, looking to satisfy their ravenous appetites. Mieke panicked. "We've got to get inside!"

Flor could hear the men's voices and the sound of crashing glass as the mob moved swiftly, looting the houses along their deserted street. "God help us!" she cried as she pushed her neighbors through the front door where *Baboe* and the children stood waiting. Her trusted servant bolted the door behind them.

Flor snapped orders. "Children, close all shutters! The windows! The curtains! Someone — Pier, quickly lock the kitchen door! Everybody, get away from the windows!"

"Mama! Mama!" Ineke grabbed her mother's legs and hid her face in Flor's dress. Eighteen-month-old Jantine sat cowering on Yelly's lap. The eldest Giliam daughter attempted to comfort her with soothing words, yet the baby's wails continued.

A sudden bang outside, followed by the shouting of men, startled everyone in the house. The mob had arrived.

Crash! A school window shattered next door. Clang! A rock found its mark on the lamp post outside the house.

The dog could not be restrained. He bounded energetically toward the front door baring his teeth and barking. The youngest children began to bawl as Flor herded her brood behind the flimsy rattan furniture. Mieke held her two children tightly in her arms.

Corrie sat, her knees curled to her chin, rocking rhythmically under the kitchen table. *"We gaan allemaal sterven! Allemaal dood* [We're all going to die. Everyone dead]!" she lamented as her boys huddled by her side.

The vandals hurled rocks against the house and shouted obscenities. The sound of thuds against the walls seemed amplified indoors.

Flor, trembling, knew of only one thing to do at that moment. "Come, let's pray." The children clung to her every word. Though frightened and whimpering, they folded their hands expectantly. Yelly, head bowed, still had an arm wrapped around weeping Jantine.

Flor uttered a quick and simple prayer. "Dear heavenly Father, please send your angels to protect us and our home, in Jesus' name."

"Di sana [Over there]!" The shrill voice of the mob leader uttered a command above the raucous shouting of the men outside.

Several voices repeated the command. Then momentary silence. "What's happening?" whispered Mieke. The throbbing gang of bare-breasted looters had suddenly become distracted. Their voices and the thumping of feet faded as they retreated down the street.

Flor, the children, and the two neighbor families remained crouched in hiding until peace settled over them. The mission home had served well as a refuge. "Children," Flor was the first to speak. "This is a miracle."

With a sigh of relief, she continued, "Dear Heavenly Father, You have answered our prayers again. Thank you for protecting us. We are grateful. In Jesus' name. Amen."

For now, they were safe. But as evening fell, a foreboding darkness descended on Gombong.

～

IN THE FLICKERING GLOW OF A BRASS OIL LAMP, FLOR, MIEKE AND Corrie sat across from each other sipping tea in the sitting room, their faces sullen. The children were in bed. Outside the choir of chirping crickets competed against the drone of the cicadas under the full moon.

"Those wretched vandals will be back again," Mieke broke the silence. "What are we going to do?"

"I am going to demand help from Keboemen. I must speak to the *Wedena* [Mayor]. Only he can assist us."

Flor knew that venturing into the streets would put her in great danger, but she saw no alternative. Perhaps the Dutch authorities in Keboemen, who still had a unit of motorcycle police patrolmen, could help.

Mieke set down her cup and sat back astonished. "See the *Wedena*? Flor! It's far too dangerous!"

"Mieke, I think it's best I leave right away," Flor continued.

"Now? In the dark?" Mieke objected in alarm.

"It's safer than in daylight when the gangs can see me. Maybe I can take the dog for protection."

"No, Flor! Please don't go!" Mieke entreated. She reached out a hand and laid it on the table in front of her in an effort to calm her friend. "You'll be breaking curfew!"

Flor straightened in her seat. "At least I have to try," she said kindly. "Who else will help us?"

She pushed back her chair and calmly strode to a small, wooden wall mirror. Turning her head to the side, she examined her reflection, repositioning the pins holding her hair in a bun. She

adjusted her round, metal-rimmed glasses and gazed searchingly at herself.

Was this the same Flor that had looked back at her mere months
ago? Would she be making a decision like this if Menno were
here? Most assuredly not.

Corrie approached in short, shuffling steps and touched Flor's
arm lightly. She pressed her dog's lead into her hand. Flor
nodded.

"Oh! I so wish you wouldn't go!" whined Mieke.

Baboe was also distraught. "Be careful *mevrouw.*"

Flor gazed adoringly at her dear friends. Their somber faces
were tense with angst, yet they admired her courage.

"If I don't go, we could all be slaughtered. I must go."

Flor leaned forward and gave Mieke a kiss on each cheek, then
nodded to Corrie. "Ladies, please take care of my children ... if I
get delayed."

Baboe unbolted the front door. Flor straightened her skirt, and
with the neighbor's loyal German Shepherd by her side, took a
deep breath and stepped cautiously into the shadowy street.

8

LIFE IN PERIL

POW CAMP, SURABAYA, EAST JAVA

December 6, 1942

… Mijn schat [my darling], I see myself in a different light now that I have been wrestling with these matters so often and have talked it over with friends … how I realize my shortcomings. You have forgiven me already, haven't you Flor?

My biggest mistake has been my self-centeredness. Whether I was conscious or not, my actions flowed out of what I wanted to do, when I wanted to do it … I realize now that my attitude towards God was the cause of this egocentricity.

My dear Flor, the bright side of all this is that there may still be time left for us and our children to live to God's glory and honor. This very hope will keep me going.

… Flor, suppose we would have had the perfect marriage, the best possible relationship two people could ever have with each other. Yet, it did not have the most important component of all — a love towards God. Wouldn't we fall back into the same situation as before …

Oh yes, He was important to us, but He definitely was not the source of our existence ... But because that did not take place, we soon ran into problems. Now, I thank God for this time of reflections.

My sweet, sweet, little Flor. You are the wife given to me by God, received from Him, the greatest gift for a man here on earth. But so often I didn't consider you to be just that. I didn't honor you the way I should have.

This is what God has shown me here, again.

~

DECEMBER 7, 1942

... Oh, I just love writing something to you this way each day, to think of you, to do something that will later prove how often my thoughts were with you when you read the notes yourself.

... I believe ... our lives and the lives of our children lie completely in God's hands. He will give us the strength, whatever the future holds, even in our suffering to endure all to His honor.

~

HER SENSES HEIGHTENED, FLOR STRODE AT A QUICK STEADY PACE, contending only with the occasional mosquito in the humid night air. "*Hond* [Dog], not much further," she muttered as they neared the bend leading to the *Wadena's* home. The old dog wagged his tail and looked up trustingly.

In the moonlight she saw the stately, white stucco home of the mayor of Gombong. Flor approached with caution, stepping up to the carved wooden front door. She set her hand on the iron knocker and with a deep breath brought it down repeatedly. The hollow clanging echoed in the night. Flor stepped back and waited, taking in the scents and shadowy beauty of the manicured gardens in the moonlight.

The door slowly creaked open. Two dark brown eyes peered through the crack from behind a chain and spotted Flor.

"Huh?" A male voice grunted incredulously.

The door swung open to reveal an astonished pudgy, balding, gray-haired mayor staring at her. Scratching his goatee nervously, he said, *"Mevrouw!* What are you doing here in the middle of the night? You could be killed!"

"Meneer, you must help me," Flor pleaded, "I have eleven children and five women in my home here in Gombong. Please, we need you to protect us!"

"You are still in Gombong?" The mayor was shocked. "Looters are stealing everything in sight and murdering the Europeans who haven't fled."

"I know, *Meneer!* I am only asking that you phone the government officials in Keboemen. Please, ask them to send us police protection."

The mayor studied his feet for a moment but shook his head. "Sorry. I can't help you," he said dismissively. "I have more pressing matters." He stepped back to close the door.

"Please, *Meneer Wedena!"* Flor stood her ground. "Just a phone call?"

The mayor sputtered at Flor's effrontery, *"Mevrouw,* go home and take care of your household!"

"But *Meneer Wedena* ..."

"Good night, *mevrouw!"* Fuming he slammed the door.

Deep heaviness settled on Flor as she walked back to her house. She had risked her life but hadn't accomplished anything.

In the days that followed, the situation deteriorated rapidly. Soon looters had ransacked almost every residence along Gombong's main street until the neighborhood resembled a war zone. Gangs took up vigil near the mission home, unnerving everyone. Fear and panic were their constant companions until Flor could tolerate it no more. Once again she decided to go speak to the *Wedena*. *Maybe he will be more sympathetic,* she thought.

Again, Flor found herself face to face with the mayor, but this time, in his office. When she entered, he exclaimed,"*Mevrouw!* You have returned? I forbid you to come here again. You are in terrible danger!" He followed his rebuke with stories of theft, vandalism, and murders committed by the looters.

Again, Flor pleaded with him to contact the authorities in Keboemen for help. Moved by her determination, the mayor appeared more amenable to her plight. "Let me send wagons to fetch you and your children, and the others who are with you." He responded. "You will be safer in Keboemen. Go home and get ready. Help will arrive in a few hours."

Flor rushed home with the message. It was early afternoon, so she and Mieke frantically prepared to leave. *Kokkie* had set a table for a midday meal, but in all the activity, no one ate.

Flor had already sewn small homemade backpacks for each child to wear. She dressed the children, put sun hats on their heads, packed their bags and strapped them to their backs. The children sat waiting eagerly for the wagons.

With preparations complete, Flor and Mieke had time to contemplate their situation.

"Do they allow civilians to travel on the main road to Keboemen?" Mieke asked.

"No, I don't think so," said Flor pensively. "The main road is only used by the military now. The wagons won't be allowed on it. We'll have to travel the rural route, and that could take many hours. I'm not sure just how safe those roads will be."

Mieke looked at the large clock on the sitting room wall. "It's already four o'clock," she noted. "In two hours it'll be dark. You know what happens after dark."

"Yes — we'll be on the road with *rampassers!*" Flor responded, her face drawn. "I don't have a good feeling about this."

"We could be risking our lives," said Mieke softly.

Soon the beat of horses' hooves sounded in the street. Flor peered out the shuttered window. "The wagons are coming. We have to decide now. Mieke, I don't think we should go."

It was an agonizing decision, yet they agreed to abandon the trip. But how to explain that to the children? The wagons looked beautiful, and after many weeks of being housebound, the children were eager for an adventure. They just couldn't understand the adults' indecisive behavior. Weepy three-year-old Ineke was inconsolable.

Flor tried to explain to the wagon drivers why they couldn't take the trip to Keboemen at this time and gave them some money for their trouble. Yet the question remained. What were they to do? It was suicidal just to wait. There had to be another way, and she knew it meant visiting the mayor's office again.

The *Wedena's* face flared at the sight of Flor, when she reappeared in his office. He was furious. "After refusing the wagons, you have the nerve to return?" Flor interrupted to explain why they had declined his generous offer and apologized for wasting his time.

Since civilians did not have phones, she again asked if he could make a call to the authorities in Keboemen. Her persistence had worn him down. The mayor consented without argument and handed her the phone.

Flor dialed the number given to her, reached the Regent's Office of the District of Keboemen, and expressed her concern.

"*Mevrouw!*" said a stern male voice. "Under what authority do you take upon yourself to call this office? You are completely out of order to do such a thing. We are not authorized to send help, and I would appreciate if you would kindly respect the authorities. We are involved in more urgent matters."

89

Before Flor could protest, he added, "Don't you know that seventy soldiers have stayed behind in Gombong to protect you — civilians? Why are you bothering us?"

"With all due respect, *meneer*," she objected, "perhaps you are unaware that all those men have fled. So where is our protection?"

Flor was angry. A sudden boldness surged from within. "Furthermore, I want you to know something *meneer*, so please listen carefully.

"When my husband was called to active service with the Dutch forces last December, he did not question whether or not to go. It was his duty. He left with full confidence that the country he was defending would protect his wife and children during times of great danger.

"*Meneer*, those times have arrived. We are in great danger! And you are telling me that the country my husband held so dear is suggesting that his family does not have enough value to be protected? The *rampassers* are ready to take everything we own and murder us. In the event that I survive, I will report this matter to the highest officials, without delay."

Astonished by her forthrightness, the Keboemen official reconsidered. "Okay, okay, *mevrouw*. Go home quickly. I'll send help."

"*Meneer, dank u* [Mister, thank you]!" Flor hung up the phone and smiled cordially at the mayor. "They're sending help," she reported. Wide-eyed, the mayor stood to offer her a hand as she turned to leave.

∼

EARLY THE NEXT MORNING, FLOR SAT AT THE BREAKFAST TABLE savoring a cup of coffee and discussing the previous day's events with Mieke, Corrie and the children. Though physically tired, she was mentally charged. "Keboeman agreed to send help!"

"But did they say when?" Mieke responded. "This is one of the few homes that hasn't been broken into. Yet."

Ten-year-old Pier, understanding the urgency of their needs, slipped from his chair and approached his mother.

"Mama, can Hilda and I go out and look for bottles today," he said. "Get some extra money?"

"Pier, *schat*," Flor was touched by his thoughtfulness. "I'm afraid it's too dangerous outside."

Just then two knocks sounded on the kitchen door. The women jolted. "Who could that be at this hour?" wondered Flor.

Baboe reached for the front shutters and cautiously parted them. "*Mevrouw!* It's the Chinese businessman and two young men!"

She hurried to unbolt the front door as Flor quickly dismissed the children and followed her.

Without offering a greeting, the businessman thrust a wad of Indies notes toward Flor. "One hundred guilders. I buy cabinet."

Flor was thrilled but masked her excitement. With all the mouths to feed, the cash was timely. She took the bills and casually counted them. It wouldn't be wise to appear too needy lest he change his mind.

"Follow me, gentlemen." Flor tucked the cash into her skirt pocket and lead the Chinese man and his two companions to the cabinet in the sitting room.

He bent over and studied it closely. With his head to one side, he ran his fingers over its carved edges.

"It's in excellent condition. You've done well, *meneer*. Got yourself a bargain," Flor assured him.

Satisfied, the businessman smiled broadly and directed the two Chinese youths to come. They picked it up at each end and lugged the cabinet to the door. He followed but stopped at Menno's mahogany radio.

"Two hundred guilders?" he offered, pointing to it.

"For the radio?" That was out of the question. It was their lifeline to the outside world. And besides, it held great value to Menno. "I'm afraid it's not for sale, *meneer*," Flor answered curtly. "It's my husband's."

He reached to stroke the radio's beautiful mahogany wood.

"*Not* for sale!" Flor was firm.

Quickly retracting his hand, he bowed politely and hurried along behind the hired help. Flor bolted the door behind him and leaned against it in disbelief. *What an unexpected blessing!* she mused and patted the wad of Indies guilders in her skirt pocket.

Mieke approached shaking her head. "Didn't think we'd see him again! Flor, when you and your children pray ... "

Flor had barely walked away from the door when a violent tumult erupted at the front of the house. The Chinese businessman cursed in Malay. Enraged men shouted. A front window shattered under a volley of rocks, as frenzied looters, exposed by the businessman, seemed determined to break in.

Flor ducked into the sitting room. The children ran to her, frightened by the screaming and rocks.

"Children, everyone, under the table! *Baboe*, secure the doors!" Flor ordered. Jantine and Ineke began to wail. The other children pressed in next to Corrie under the table, weeping softly.

"God help us!" Mieke panicked. Both she and Flor lived in constant fear knowing they couldn't defend themselves. They prayed continually for protection, the children being their main concern. The women would have given their lives for their safety.

While everyone hurried to take cover, a low, rolling rumble of vehicles sounded outside. Pier, unable to contain his curiosity, ran to the shuttered window to peek through. "Mama!" he yelled. "It's the police on motorcycles! I think they're coming to help us!"

Flor hurried to the window and bent over him to look. Half a dozen Dutch soldiers were riding down the street toward the mission home. They approached quickly, rifles strapped to their sides, honking in an attempt to disperse the mob.

"Pier, come! Let's get away from the window," The two joined the rest of the group. Everyone strained to hear what was happening outside.

The motorcycles screeched to a halt in front of the house. The riders dismounted, commanding the *rampassers* to leave, but the defiant mob refused to obey. They escalated their anger and aggression, some picking up stones to throw at the soldiers, others yelling loud obscenities. The police couldn't gain control.

Several sudden rifle retorts sounded. Warning shots? Flor and Mieke looked at each other.

Suddenly, deafening bursts of gunfire erupted. The women and children covered their ears. The German Shepherd barked incessantly.

The onslaught continued for what seemed like an unbearably long time. Then suddenly, all went quiet. The motorcycles revved to life and roared off, the sound of their engines receding.

Shaken and emotionally spent, the children still sniffling, clung to each other, and the women cried in one another's arms. With the respite came the overwhelming conviction that God had spared them — again.

The children crawled out of hiding first.

Mieke, followed by three boys and Flor, took the lead to venture onto the veranda. Mieke shrieked. Flor covered her mouth, sickened by the sight. Twenty-three bloodied male islanders lay dead in the street.

To Flor's disbelief, the bodies remained there in the hot sun for days, rotting and emitting a foul stench, until finally the authorities came to collect them.

Despite these traumatic events, peace settled on the mission home. The Dutch military erected a small guard house across the street, and the soldiers occasionally visited Flor and Mieke to enjoy casual conversation over coffee. But the welcomed protection was short-lived. Since no further incidents occurred on the street, the soldiers were reassigned to another section of Gombong the following week.

For a little while all was peaceful, but Flor and Mieke awakened one night to the rhythmic sound of a tong-tong — a traditional Indies instrument. Unable to sleep, they went into the sitting room.

"What can it mean?" asked Mieke.

Flor shrugged. "Maybe it's a warning?" She could only guess. But with it came the familiar, unwelcome fear of impending danger.

Together they sat listening to the persistent, foreboding sound. "I feel uncomfortable, Mieke. Maybe we should wake the children just in case we have to be ready to leave quickly."

Mieke agreed.

Everyone gathered in the sitting room and waited. The sound continued. Flor, concerned, looked at each of the tired faces — sleepy children huddled together, their heads on each other's shoulders, completely at the mercy ... of what? Suddenly she felt overwhelmed with responsibility for their welfare. If they were in danger, should she just sit and allow it to arrive? Flor stood to her feet. She would not submit to hopelessness. Once again, in the darkness she set out for the mayor's house.

Flor shivered. The night air seemed dark and eerie. She strode cautiously along the familiar dirt road past a patch of dense trees and squinted at the driveway leading to the mayor's house. An unusually bright light, such as she'd never seen before, illuminated it.

Suddenly a twig snapped in the bushes behind her. Flor froze in her tracks. Cold fear washed over her and every muscle tensed. She turned quickly but couldn't see anyone. Her mind raced. Was it the enemy? Was the mayor's house under assault? Maybe just an animal?

"Jij daar! Kom hier [You over there! Come here]!" She jolted. A Dutch voice spoke from behind a bush.

Was it a trap? Flor had no option but to obey. Her wobbly legs propelled her forward.

A young KNIL soldier in his twenties rose to his feet. *"Mevrouw!* What are you doing here in the middle of the night? You're risking your life!"

Flor's eyes filled with tears of relief. "I … I'm on my way to speak to the *Wedena*," she answered, her mouth still dry from fear.

"The *Wedena*? Now? He's not going to like that!"

"Please, *meneer!*" Flor begged. "I have eleven children and five adults in my home in Gombong! We fear for our lives. We need help! I must speak to the *Wedena*."

The young soldier's voice softened. "Come. It's best I escort you home. It's safer." He was kind and friendly and listened with interest to Flor's story.

"Maybe I was sent here just to protect you and your children," the young Dutchman mused. "Our company was assigned to halt the rioting and looting. We just arrived in Gombong earlier today. I'll tell you what. I'll arrange for your house to be put under a twenty-four-hour watch."

"Oh, *meneer!* Thank you!" Flor was relieved and grateful, particularly when he added a pan of rice to his benevolence.

That was one of Flor's last encounters with Dutch soldiers. The Japanese soon captured all remaining KNIL fighters and sent them to POW camps. In their place, Japanese fighters arrived dressed only in black loincloths. The Dutch women, bred with European decorum, were shocked at such revealing undress.

Flor's world had morphed so quickly. She slumped in despair unable to shake the nagging sense that far more unsettling changes were yet to come.

9

THE EMPEROR RULES

POW CAMP, SURABAYA, EAST JAVA

December 9, 1942

It's not easy to find time to write here. Yesterday morning and afternoon I worked in the peanut factory for a while, but I felt ill later in the day. I was suffering from a bad case of diarrhea and stomach cramps. Last night, I got an injection and I'll get a second one today. I've lost quite a bit of weight here. How about you? How are you? You need all the strength and courage possible to endure this dark hour.

Oh Flor, if I didn't know that our King was standing beside you, knowing your needs and able to carry your load, I would be ready to give up in despair. Will He not help His children? You and also our precious little ones? Flor, how are they doing? My soul cries out in great pain when I think about all of you. I deeply long for you.

Last night, I dreamed about you. It was not a nice dream ... I was there just like the man I used to be, with all my shortcomings. But I believe that through these hard times, we will be allowed to walk the straight path again.

I'm not too concerned about my health, although it leaves a lot to be desired. What worries me more is the fact that my heart isn't right yet.

I so desire that the depth of my being would reflect a change so that my dreams would reveal that new spirit. Oh, that our lives would reflect God's character!

My dearest Flor, they are announcing that the doctor is on his way and in a little while it will be dark because of blackout procedures. My sweetheart, bye, for now, your Menno and Papa.

∼

December 9, 1942

Dear Flor,

Just a while ago, I whistled the song, "A Mighty Fortress is Our God, a bulwark never failing ... " And thought of you. Oh, my sweet little bride! You were a beautiful rose not fully opened yet. How I should have taken care of that beauty and how I should have carefully encouraged it even more. But Flor, the bonds that held me captive were so strong ...

If I would be without God now, then things would be quite intolerable. But with our bulwark never failing – who will surely be our helper – everything will be all right.

My little bride, your Menno.

∼

December 10, 1942

How did things go with you today, Flor, and with the kids? Quite tough, isn't it? With the help of our heavenly Father, you will have come through. I hardly even worry about you Flor, because I know the Lord is taking care of you.

∼

DECEMBER 12, 1942

Today, I got my fifth injection. I'm becoming nice and slim, weighing 78 kg. Not bad, heh? Flor, if only I felt a little stronger again, but I'm sure every detail of our lives is being looked after and I'm quite optimistic. I have a nice little book here, which I have just finished reading. The young wife in that story reminded me so much of you. If God would grant us this grace, that one day we would be reunited, what a wonderful joy that would be!

Imagine being united again with the children, especially the older ones, who will then be able to get to know their father again. I will have been tried and purified through the hardships of this camp. From then on, I will pray every day that God would keep us from trying to live in our own strength ...

My little wife, if I had only treated you the way I should have, especially during your difficult periods of pregnancy, our lives would have been so much richer, my love. And yet, to make you and I ready for our eternal home, we have had to go through this deep valley. In due time, schat, we will come to know God's words, "Comfort, ye, comfort ye, my people, you have received double out of the hand of the Lord for all your sins." (Isaiah 40)

~

LIFE IN THE JAPANESE POW CAMP AT SURABAYA WAS GRUELING AND unpleasant. Menno received another severe beating when the notebook with his children's birth dates was discovered and confiscated. Would he dare write more letters to Flor? How he longed to speak to her in person.

With long workdays and inadequate food, hunger and exhaustion plagued the prisoners. Meals were unimaginative — pitifully small portions of rice and mixed greens. The men routinely returned from work to the internment camp ravenously hungry.

At six o'clock, dusk fell, and all went dark. The POWs tried to rest, but the sweltering heat and food cravings made sleeping on beds constructed from rough, bamboo planks difficult.

One night a large rat sniffing the ground below the POWs jumped onto Menno's bunk. It eyed his foot and clamped down hard on his big toe.

"Ouwwww!" Menno hollered and bolted upright, shaking the vermin loose. The defiant creature leaped at his face. Swatting madly in the dark, Menno flung the rodent to the floor. It scurried away, but the commotion startled awake the groggy POWs in adjacent bunks.

"Hey ... Giliam!" De Wit, leaning on his elbow, sounded annoyed. "What's going on? Having a bad dream?"

"Rat bit my toe!" Menno mumbled, trying to examine the injury in the dark.

"A rat bit your boney toe?" exclaimed de Graaf, alarmed, yet never missing an opportunity for humor. "Even the rats here are starving!"

The other men snickered and drifted back to sleep.

Traumatized, Menno lay wide awake. He missed Flor and the children and hoped with all his heart that their circumstances were better than his.

THE SUMMER OF 1942 WAS HOT, LONG AND LONELY IN OCCUPIED Gombong. Japanese soldiers arrived unannounced one day to confiscate not just the family's refrigerator, but Menno's prized radio — without compensation. Flor was heartbroken. She watched helplessly as her captors carried it away. Clearly, those who remained in Gombong were being systematically forced into isolation from the rest of the world.

Without the means to keep food from spoiling, yet needing to feed twelve people within her care, Flor searched for ways to be resourceful. When she ran out of Australian flour, she replaced it with rice — for breakfast rice porridge, rice with vegetables in the afternoon, and for dinner, the family favorite, *nasi goreng* (fried rice).

The daily challenges of survival were something even the children were willing to embrace. They helped collect bottles to earn money and diligently handed their income to Flor.

With increased seclusion came an ever-growing presence of Japanese guards. Stationed throughout the city, their presence created a sense of dread, and an expectation for even more changes. Eventually they took possession of the mission school and used it for mandatory Japanese language lessons. Flor, Mieke, and their good friend Marjan de Vries, along with the rest of the remnant of Dutch women in Gombong, were forced to attend classes there.

The women, cramped into the child-sized benches, sat hungry and uninterested in learning the staccato sounds of their diminutive, dark-haired subjugators.

With a piece of chalk in hand, a bespectacled Japanese instructor scratched large characters on the black board. Using a long, wooden stick he pointed to each one, motioning for the class to repeat after him.

"Ichi, ni, san [One, two, three]."

"Ichi, ni, san [One, two, three]," the women parroted back, half-heartedly.

"Ichi, ichi, ichi [One, one, one]."

"Ichi, ichi, ichi [One, one, one]," came the unenthusiastic response.

"Ni, ni, ni [Two, two, two]!"

"Ni, ni, ni [Two ... two ... two]."

Flor rolled her eyes as she glanced at Marjan. Both began to giggle. The monotonous repetitions of the strange new words suddenly sounded comical. Like schoolgirls, they fought to gain control of their laughter.

The instructor wheeled around. Flor cupped her mouth with an embroidered handkerchief, and Mieke coughed into her hand. With a threatening glare he scanned the classroom, but the laughter had vanished, so he continued.

"*Shi, go, roku* [Four, five, six]."

With a little more energy, the women repeated, "*Shi, go roku* [Four, five, six]."

Flor quietly sighed in relief. Any sign of disrespect for the Emperor, or his emissaries warranted painful redress. They had escaped punishment this time.

Flor's thoughts wandered from the reality of their captivity to better days. This had been Menno's classroom. But where was he now? Oh, how she missed him!

As the war dragged on, the future became increasingly uncertain for the European civilians on Java. Rumors began to circulate that they would soon be interned, but no one knew when. For most, money had run out and food had become scarce, making day to day living a challenge. Yet, people reasoned, surely they wouldn't be abandoned to starve to death!

The monotony of life under Japanese occupation was especially hard on the children. Despite Flor's efforts to keep them occupied, they had become restless, lacking the freedom to enjoy the outdoors. They missed school, and most of all, they missed their father.

Around that time a letter arrived from friends in Wonosobo — the lush, mountainous town where they had lived previously in central Java — inviting the children to visit. Flor arranged for Pier and Hilda to go, and it turned out to be a wonderful distraction.

Pier was especially excited the day they got back. "I have a surprise for you," he said when Flor met them at the train station, "but you will have to wait till we get home."

She smiled at his enthusiasm. "Does it have something to do with that cookie jar?"

"Just wait and see," he replied, holding tightly to his treasure.

As soon as they arrived home, Pier put down his bags and turned to Flor. "Mama, here. This is something really special." He handed Flor his precious jar.

Did Pier bring some baked goods? She wondered. The bottom felt heavy. She smiled and with great interest lifted the lid.

"What?" She almost dropped the jar! Two eyes on a large, arrow-shaped face stared at her from a circle of coils underneath. Her face ashen, she caught her breath, slammed the lid back on the jar and looked in horror at Pier's eager face.

"He's our pet!" declared Hilda.

"Yah, we found him and we've been taking care of him. Can we keep him, Mama? Please?" Pier begged.

She immediately realized this creature had special meaning and she might have to swallow her intense distaste for snakes.

"We'll take care of him, we promise," Hilda urged in all sincerity.

"Yah, we know how," added Pier.

By now all the children, especially little Menno, were begging to keep the snake, so Flor conceded. Unexpectedly, it became a treasured family pet and offered Pier and Menno many hours of joy. They found it food — frogs and small creatures — and provided a closed environment for it in the garden so it could not escape.

The girls adopted pigeons and spent hours taking care of them. The social birds welcomed interaction with them, sat on their shoulders and fed from their hands. The pets eased the children's lives in the uncertain political climate.

Flor, however, grew increasingly weary from the escalating tension and worry. Survival had become the sole purpose of many, and people were resorting to whatever means they could to acquire food. Yet, ironically, the tables had turned. The rich had become poor, but among Gombong's residents, Flor was now regarded as wealthy. She was one of few still able to purchase food and other necessities.

With the year drawing to a close, the heavy tropical rainy season returned, giving the *rampassers* cover to steal what few treasures remained. The heavy downpours masked the sound of their footsteps, and break-ins became commonplace. Flor could barely sleep.

Added to her anxiety were the constant rumors that more changes were coming.

ON DECEMBER 20, 1942, A VEHICLE RAMBLED UP THE DESOLATE main street of Gombong past vandalized Dutch homes. Once emblems of a flourishing colony, they now were empty, lifeless shells. Windows shattered, shutters hanging, doors yanked off and metal ornamentation pilfered, they had become ghosts of their former glory. In the back seat of the car, sat the mayor of Gombong dressed in his off-white, three-piece suit. A stolid police officer in a formal tan uniform sat beside him, and an Indies driver was behind the wheel.

"Good God!" The mayor shook his head. The destruction of the colonial homes was extensive along the main street as they approached the mission home.

Two dark-skinned boys in shorts prodded a squawking chicken past the former Christian Dutch Indies School. A horse-drawn cart driven by a toothless, elderly local clip-clopped by, laboring under the weight of stolen Dutch furniture. The mayor felt anger rising. He instructed the driver to stop, " ... and wait here," he continued as he nervously stroked his goatee. The driver nodded, turned off the ignition, and sent a sly smile to the passing saronged looter while his passengers disembarked from the opposite side.

As the *Wedena* walked to the door, he could hear adults and children singing inside. Flor, Mieke, Corrie and the children were gathered in the sitting room, now boarded up. It was Sunday morning, the Lord's Day, and Flor was determined to continue worship as a family. Neatly dressed in church attire, they sang a hymn *a cappella*, their faces glowing in the light of a single lamp. Jantine squealed with delight as she galloped to the rhythm on Hilda's knee.

The sound of unfamiliar male voices outside sent *Baboe* scurrying to the shuttered front door. Through the slits she observed the mayor and his police escort approaching. From his crisply ironed pant pocket, he pulled a white handkerchief and wiped the sweat from his forehead.

"*Mevrouw* Giliam! It's the *Wedena!*" *Baboe* exclaimed. "And he doesn't look pleased."

Surprised, Flor stood up and smoothed her skirt. "The *Wedena?* On a Sunday morning? What can he possibly want?"

Three aggressive thumps of the knocker sounded against the front door.

"*Baboe*, please let him in," Flor instructed.

The house servant opened the door and Flor approached, her hand extended. "Meneer *Wedena!* I am so grateful for all you've done for us. Please, do come in." The mayor, his face downcast, responded only with a nod. Flor's welcoming smile faded.

Menno and Pier edged their way to their mother's side, staring wide-eyed at the pudgy man.

"*Mevrouw* Giliam. *Mevrouw* van Dijk," his gaze fixed on the boys, he addressed the women without exchanging greetings. "All European women and children must report to the Japanese commandant at the train station promptly at eight o'clock tomorrow morning."

"Train station?" Mieke repeated as if she hadn't heard correctly.

Cradling her doll, Ineke pushed in front of her older brothers. Her hazel eyes imploring the stranger.

"Where are we going?" Flor asked, rattled by the news.

The mayor could not look Flor in the eyes. "The destination has yet to be announced." His gaze settled on Ineke's innocent face. "I suggest you start packing. Each person is allowed one case. How many children do you have, *mevrouw?*"

Flor felt alarm rising. "Seven," she responded.

"Then you are allowed four mattresses. Two people per mattress. One wardrobe per family. The same for all the European guests in your house."

Yelly squeezed into the doorway holding little Jantine. The happy child smiled and extended her tiny hand. She waved to the mayor and said musically, "*Daaag! Daaag* [Hi! Hi]!"

The mayor's face tightened. He stepped back and bowed slightly. "Now, if you'll pardon me, ladies, I have more announcements ... to deliver." His voice cracked.

Turning his back abruptly to the little gathering at the front door, he started down the path. From his pocket he retrieved the handkerchief and wiped his eyes. With a nod to his police escort, he walked down the path at a brisk pace. *Baboe*, distraught, bolted the door behind him.

"Train? Mama, we're going on a train?" Menno asked, excitedly.

"To see Papa?" Pier added.

Flor half shrugged. "I ... I ... don't know ... "

She collapsed into a settee — arms and legs limp. The time had come. "Mieke, the rumors are right; we're being interned!" It was simply too much to bear. It meant leaving behind everything she knew and everything that was dear and taking her children into a future of unknown danger.

And what would she pack for seven children and herself? Where would she store the valuables left behind? Flor became paralyzed with fear at the monumental task ahead, but there wasn't a moment to spare.

"Mama, you rest. I'll get the cases ready." Instinctively Yelly sensed her mother's distress. She knelt next to her and cooled her with a Chinese hand fan.

Flor opened her eyes and stroked the long, blonde braids of her trusted eldest. Her sweet words and genuine love brought immeasurable comfort.

Mieke and Corrie left abruptly to prepare. With Yelly's help, Flor soon pulled herself together and began to pack mechanically. Together they sorted clothing and filled suitcases well into the night — one piece of luggage per person. Four mattresses and a wardrobe would be shipped later.

But what to do with valuable items they couldn't take? Flor and Yelly decided to send some to the missionary hospital in Keboemen. They left others with their trusted friend Reverend Kijlstra. Documents and valuables they passed to a native teacher for safekeeping. Emergency food supplies, cutlery, linens, furniture and most of their clothing, had to be left behind.

The most painful decision, however, was what to do with the children's pets. With many tears they said goodbye to their beloved pigeons and snake, leaving the creatures in the care of a Chinese teacher.

With the packing complete, Yelly trudged wearily to bed, but Flor, now alone, stole a moment to appreciate the life God had given them at the mission house. It was rich with treasured family memories. With a heavy heart, she trod softly to the children's bedrooms to cherish the sight of them sleeping peacefully in the home they had come to love. "Whatever lies ahead, Lord, please protect us," she whispered. "Watch over the children."

Flor retired to her bedroom. Still one more important thing to do.

Sliding open the bottom drawer of Menno's handcrafted wooden desk, she lifted out his metal safe. From it she extracted a folded bundle of Indies guilders — money she would take for emergencies. Flor knew if she was caught hiding money, she would be punished by the Japanese, but she was willing to take the risk for the survival of her children.

Carefully she flattened the paper notes and sewed them into the hems of her floral dresses. Satisfied the money was well hidden, she rolled a few more bills and inserted them into the center of spools of thread. Others she flattened and hid inside her purse lining. The remaining money she folded and gently pressed into the bottom of an ointment bottle.

She shuddered. "Oh Lord, don't let them find the money!"

Just before she lay down for the last time in her comfortable bed, she tucked her tiny Bible — her most important possession — gently into the bottom of her purse.

~

POW Camp, Surabaya, East Java

December 13, 1942

There are several things I wish to share with you, my dearest wife. You always have, and always will be the love of my life, my pearl, my ruby, the joy of my heart with love overflowing.

This morning I went to church. It was just great. Just now, I had a talk with the pastor. My soul shouts with joy that our God is a God who helps us, takes care of us so well, and who forgives all our sins – all of them – each and every one of them, for He knows them all … He covers us with this love, and we hide under His wings until the storm has passed.

And after all the sorrow I caused you, I still know that you love me and that you are looking forward to my homecoming. Dear Flor, in the same way (how is it possible?) our Heavenly Father is longing greatly for us to come to Him, lost sons and daughters. Shout for joy, shout! There is joy with God's angels for the lost that return. Flor, what a great wonder of wonders!

Are you having a pleasant Sunday, Flor, and the children too? Have you been able to go to a service today? The day is almost over. It's supper time, rice porridge with sugar. I have to go my dearest one.

Love from your own Menno.

~

DECEMBER 14, 1942

Oh, my Flor, how much better I'm feeling today. I thoroughly enjoyed the meager meal. Imagine the complaints that would have accompanied this kind of food before all this happened!

Tomorrow I'm hoping to be back at work. How worthwhile we will consider this time in retrospect, for it has allowed us to see the things that really matter and it has given us an overwhelming sense of thankfulness towards our Heavenly Father. Oh, but I do hope it will not be long now before this time will be over …

~

DECEMBER 15, 1942

Yesterday, I worked at the peanut factory all day. I still felt a bit weak, but it wasn't too bad. They allowed me to take home two pounds of peanut butter. What a treasure! I only ate a tiny bit, but my stomach and intestines weren't able to digest it. I have diarrhea again, which means bed rest the whole day. The doctor was here this morning and he will do his best to give me a little bit of butter every day from the hospital so that I might get used to something rich again.

I find this quite ironic. I have an abundance of protein now, but I cannot tolerate it anymore. And yet, Flor, I feel fine. God the Lord, my covenant God, it is He that cares for me. Even without fat or butter, He can keep me standing.

How are you doing today and how are the children? My dearest one, I hope that you are still strong and able to do all that you have to do, especially the enormous task of looking after the children by yourself in wartime.

Now I want to say a special hello to all, starting with you schat, Mom, then my sweet little Yelly, my Pier, my favorite Pil [Hilda], and Menno, my sweet little Anneke, my dear Ientje [Ineke], and then my darling Jantine. Oh, my eight darlings, not to be bought with gold, received from God.

When I had you so close, I didn't appreciate you enough, but as I sit here in Surabaya, in this small barrack and with stern guards walking around me, I now realize all that God has given to me. It doesn't matter what happens if only one day I could receive you all back. Bye for now, Flor. Your truly loving Menno.

10

DESTINATION UNKNOWN

KEBOEMEN, CENTRAL JAVA, DECEMBER 1942

The distant crowing of a rooster punctuated the relentless early morning buzz of the cicadas. It had been an exhausting night for the hundreds of Europeans gathered at the Keboemen train station. After travelling by rail from Gombong during the early hours of the previous day, the women and children spent the night in an empty oil factory in Keboemen. Sleeping on the concrete floor, their backpacks served as pillows.

The sky glowed red along the horizon signally day break, and Flor sat down on her sturdy hard case and propped up dozing Jantine on her lap. Under the surveillance of Japanese guards, she surreptitiously stroked the hem of her floral pleated dress. The secret guilders, unseen, yet unmistakable to touch, brought her a tinge of panic. What would her captors do if they discovered the money? Had she been unwise?

She reminded herself that the children must never learn of the hidden gilders. "Come, children, set your cases down." She hoped her agitation would go unnoticed. "Sit and wait here until the train comes."

Flor's daughters yielded to their mother's command. Drowsy and lethargic, they dragged their cases next to hers and plunked themselves down on them.

"I'm hungry," whined Hilda. It had been too early to eat when they left the factory. Yelly gently pulled shy Ineke onto her lap, while sleepy Anneke cuddled beside them.

The boys arrived and dropped their cases. Spotting the rail line, they raced off to kick stones onto the tracks.

Mieke trailed behind with her children, stumbling under the weight of their heavy luggage. Fearing exposure to the tropical sun, fair-skinned Mieke was conspicuously adorned with her husband's military hard cap. With a sigh of relief, she dropped her case and motioned to her children. "Inge! Bram! Come join Tante Flor. Take a seat here and rest for a while."

Six-year-old Bram wasn't happy. He rubbed his belly. *"Mama, Ik heb honger. Wanneer gaan we eten* [Mama, I am hungry. When are we going to eat]?"

"Schat, soon," Mieke tried to sound more optimistic than she felt. "We'll all get something soon."

Just then the familiar figures of Doctor de Jong and Reverend Kijlstra came into view weaving through the crowd of Dutch women and children.

"Mevrouw Giliam! *Mevrouw* van Dijk!" called the doctor, waving over people's heads.

The minister arrived carrying a small basket of warm *lumpias.* The aroma of the sticky rice delicacy covered in banana leaves turned heads.

"We're so glad we found you!" he exclaimed. "We brought gifts from the islanders at the mission. They're all terribly saddened by what is happening."

The doctor pointed to the basket. *"Kijk kinderen* [Look children]! *Lumpias!* One for each of you!" The sleepy young ones quickly awakened and enthusiastically devoured the comforting food. Pier and Menno, seeing the activity, eagerly returned from the tracks.

Lost in the delight of their warm breakfast, the family hardly noticed the exquisite, gold-trimmed luggage that plopped on the ground next to Flor. Two high society women had arrived — a tall, thin middle-aged woman wearing a fox collar and stylish heels, accompanied by her short, boisterous friend in meticulously applied make-up. Both looked miserable and awkwardly out of place.

Flor caught the conversation of the tall woman in mid-sentence: " ... silver candlesticks went to my *Baboe*. We hid the crystal in the cellar."

Her diminutive friend barely listened. "Japs better not steal my sitting room curtains. Cost me a fortune," she huffed. "Imported from Damascus!"

Flor and the minister exchanged glances. The two women seemed oblivious to the perils that lay ahead. Trying to stay upbeat, Reverend Kijlstra said, "Ladies, before you leave, why don't we all sing the *Wilhelmus*."

Mieke and Flor agreed. They rose to their feet, stood erect, and sang the Dutch national anthem. Others joined in on the second stanza:

> *... Mijn schild ende betrouwen,*
> *Zijt Gij, O God mijn Heer.*
> *Op U zo wil ik bouwen,*
> *Verlaat mij nimmermeer...*

> [... My shield and my fortress,
> Art Thou, O Lord my God.
> It is you on whom I build my hope,
> Never leave me nor forsake me ...]

Flor imagined that for the rest of her life, the Dutch national anthem would evoke the same intense emotions she felt at the train station that morning and bring to mind the scene in front of her — anxious women and children about to embark on a frightening, unknown journey, bravely singing in honor of God and country.

As they sang, the train rumbled into the station, and suddenly, like a sleeping beast, the Japanese awakened. The atmosphere shifted immediately. Barking incomprehensible orders, and waving their rifles, they cut short the singing of the anthem and shoved women and children toward the tracks.

The children licked the remaining rice kernels from the banana leaves, and along with Flor, turned to wave a last good-bye to the doctor and the minister — two stalwart men whom Flor greatly admired. Would she ever see them again? Surrounded by the anxious faces of her compatriots, she jostled forward with the crowd. Christmas 1942 was rapidly approaching. *What will the new year bring?* Flor wondered.

∿

DECEMBER 19, 1942

… Oh, if only I could have one glimpse of you now. If I just knew how things were with you, that you were all right and safe. How I dream of being home for Christmas, but I'm beginning to doubt that now.

Yesterday morning something very unpleasant happened. My best friend, de Graaf, who sleeps to my right, received quite a flogging. When the Jap suddenly appeared, no one made a move. The Jap looked around for just a minute until his gaze rested on de Graaf, probably because he was the tallest of us all. He then proceeded to give him a hard blow in the face, but de Graaf, who felt totally innocent … addressed the Jap saying, "Well, if you think that I've done something wrong, then here is my other cheek. You may hit that one as well." The Jap became furious and started to hit de Graaf everywhere with a rifle, especially against his bare shins. I was standing very close. He could have picked me instead. I felt really badly for him ... And yet, we are asked to pray for our enemies ...

～

December 21, 1942

My dearest Flor,

It's Monday night. We had a nice Sunday yesterday. We enjoyed an informal meeting with the army chaplain. How is everything with you my darling? How long, we wonder? My Flor, when I return home, how shall I find you? Blossoming and happy or aged and gray from all your worries? And our little ones, what will they be like? I sometimes wonder if they will recognize me!

It's amazing how well I'm feeling again — quite a bit slimmer, but not older — that's my vanity speaking. Mijn schatjes, what a great reunion it will be! God willing.

～

December 22, 1942

My Dear Flor,

How are you doing today and how are my darling children? You don't have to worry about me. Today, I was busy working at the peanut factory. We make about 500 jars of peanut butter per day, each weighing 500 grams. If you work at the factory, you receive one free jar a week and you are allowed to buy another jar also, while everyone else only gets a chance every ten days to buy one. We have to work hard for all of this, but at least there is the advantage to working at the factory. We hope that things will continue this way until we leave.

Oh Flor, lately I am feeling down. All of you are on my mind, but especially you Flor, with your heavy task in this difficult time. And if I let myself begin to imagine how difficult it could still get and how long it could take before we see each other, my heart shrinks with fear and worry. My soul cries out, "Lord, come and help us soon. Save us before we are no more and sink in these tempestuous seas of our lives."

And yet, Flor, if we didn't have the assurance that our God is the King who rules over everything and who knows all things, then we would be delivered into the hands of men. Then we would say with [King] David, "We are so afraid." But He saves and cares for us.

Dear Flor, God found it necessary to try me, and it was so very necessary to try me. Oh, how much better I would feel now if I had just treated you a little more lovingly! How often you asked me to go for a walk with you and the kids, but that was the last thing I felt like doing. I was sure that there were more important things to do. But above all, I despair about my attitude towards God! "Oh Lord, forgive our, yes especially my sins and trespasses." Oh, how awful it is to think about my terrible behavior of former days.

Flor, do you think of me that way with all my shortcomings, weaknesses and selfishness and does it still hurt you? Oh, my darling little children, how I would have liked to treat you more kindly, but now it is too late. Oh, my God, have mercy on us.

Christmas is coming, give us peace in our hearts. Oh Father, grant us a true celebration of Christmas and above all, give my darlings a wonderful feast. You are our God. You have all the power, this time Your will be done, Father."

Bye mijn schatjes, your deeply loving father and husband, Menno.

NIGHT GAVE WAY TO DAWN, BATHING THE JAVANESE RICE FIELDS with a misty early morning coolness. It was January 5, 1943. Menno strained under the weight of his military hard case. It had been a long, arduous march across the rolling countryside.

Wearing cropped, faded trousers spattered with mud, a scrawny Indies farmer emerged from the ethereal mist, guiding his wood plow behind a plodding ox. Bare-breasted, he sloshed ankle-deep through a soaked rice paddy when unexpected movement along the road caught his eye.

Hundreds of unshaven Dutch soldiers toiled along the rain-soaked dirt road intersecting the paddy fields. Weary and subdued from marching all night under the hostile eyes of their Japanese captors, they paraded past the farmer. The POWs carried heavy canvas duffel bags slung on their backs, their uniforms clinging to their drenched bodies. The men were on the first leg of their journey to Singapore.

Starting October, hundreds of prisoners had been shipped to more permanent POW camps, many, rumors said, to other countries. Menno reflected on Surabaya. Not knowing what lay ahead, he was glad to leave. It had been a terrible place. His thoughts wandered to the time some marines were discovered with hidden weapons. They had been punished mercilessly, some even tortured.

"*Isoide! Hayaku ike* [Hurry! Go faster]!" Startled back to the present, Menno saw a stalky Japanese soldier up ahead butt his rifle against a sickly POW struggling to keep up. The Dutch soldier teetered from the assault, and collapsed, his hard case crashing open in the mud.

Ignoring the plight of their Dutch comrade, the POWs, heads hanging, kept marching, some trampling his belongings. Menno, de Graaf and de Wit stopped.

"Looks like you're having a rough time." Menno bent down and extended a hand.

The sick man painfully cranked his muddy head toward him, his eyes terrified and desperate. He tried to speak but produced a barely audible moan. De Graaf and de Wit scrambled to gather his soaked belongings while Menno carefully lifted him to his feet. Together they wove back into the procession.

∽

EN ROUTE TO SINGAPORE

January 5, 1943

To mijn schatjes,

On January 4th we left Surabaya [POW camp]. I'm glad the trip is behind us. The evening of the 5th we arrived at the station absolutely soaked. From there we still had to walk about six kilometers.

We are now only allowed to take as much as we can carry ourselves. So yesterday, I had to dispose of practically all my belongings except for the bare essentials. The first night, because of all the rain, I had only one change of underwear left. So that's how I slept, without a blanket to keep me warm, even though it was quite cold last night. Of course, in situations like this, the diarrhea flares up. But today I have started to feel better already.

The camp here is one big mud puddle! But at least the Japanese aren't bothering us right now. We know that in a couple of days we'll have to move again, but we don't know the destination. We've all had a typhus shot, so now we simply wait for whatever may befall us. Some of our men are thinking that we'll be transported overseas, but I simply cannot believe that. I'm still very optimistic. The Lord our God will not leave us or forsake us. If only we were more aware of this and confessed it to each other.

How is everything with all of you? I refuse to believe that you have to suffer more than you are able to bear. Would a Father do that to His own children? No, for He is truly a merciful Father. Be of good courage schat [darling]. He will work it out for all of us. Bye, little ones. The Lord willing, we will see each other soon.

Your loving Menno

~

AFTER A LONG AND EXHAUSTIVE JOURNEY FROM KEBOEMEN, THE train delivered its cargo of European women and children to the town of Ambarawa, Central Java. Camp Seven, Ward Four, a former hospital converted into an internment camp, was now their "home." Surrounded by spiraling loops of barbed wire, it housed a thousand Dutch women and children.

The week that followed was marked by chaos. Flor and her family were in a small ward among seventeen adults, forty-two children and four babies. The stark room echoed like a cave. Children's shouts, and the cries of babies bounced off the walls creating a deafening noise.

The assigned space for each family was tiny. Initially, their "furniture" consisted of wooden bunk beds only. When the mattresses and wardrobe arrived a few days later, things became more manageable, but it remained a challenge for the eight Giliams to sleep on four bunk-sized mattresses.

Despite the tumultuous first week in the camp, and the passing of Christmas and New Years without much notice, Flor felt a sense of relief. The constant, debilitating fear of intruders and death was suddenly gone, along with the stress and responsibility for everyone in her household. Guards throughout the camp watched over them continually, in her perception, to protect them. That single fact lifted a huge burden, and she was able to relax and sleep soundly. Now, among other Dutch women who shared the same circumstances and experiences, she felt free, drawing strength from the others. Gone was the sense of isolation.

The children were also delighted by their new-found freedom after months of being housebound. With no toys and no responsibilities, they ran in packs to play with their many new friends. Their latest makeshift playground was a construction site for a new barrack.

Long, hastily constructed buildings with exposed wood trusses, joists and tin walls, functioned as bathing stations. In these areas, prisoners stood next to barrels, scooped and poured water over themselves to wash their hair, and rinse off the soap. The dirt floor, puddled with soapy water, was slippery in places. Early each morning, groggy internees emerged from their barracks eager to outpace the others to a bathing station.

One morning, almost three weeks after their arrival, young Menno, barefoot and dripping, emerged from the bathing area. With his towel, he wiped his boyish face framed by blond curls swept into a wet swirl. He glanced shyly at the faces of women and children in line and broke into a run back to the barracks.

Inside the family's quarters, the sound of chatter and crying babies intensified as the ward awakened. Flor felt irritated by the noise and the overcrowding. Her head ached. She was on edge.

Yelly was helping tidy their family's belongings when Menno returned. He casually handed his mother his wet towel.

"And the soap?" she asked, abruptly.

Menno remained quiet. He looked down at the floor.

"Did you forget to bring back the soap — again? Now we only have one bar left!" scolded Flor.

Menno stood frozen and ashamed. His sad eyes continued to focus on the floor, the corners of his mouth turned downward.

Flor dashed to the washing area. Frantic, she pushed past the languid women and children waiting in line. "Pardon! *Ik moet er alleen even langs. Ik hoef niet te douchen* [I just need to come through. I don't need a shower]. Sorry!"

Rushing into the bathing area, she searched hastily around each barrel, but the soap had already been snatched up. "It's gone!" She huffed, shaking her head at the sense of loss. "Will that boy ever learn?"

Flor stormed back into the barracks and marched up to Menno who sat forlorn on his bed, staring out the window.

"That's the second bar of soap you've left behind this week! If this happens again Menno, I am going to have to spank you!"

"I'm sorry, Mama," She could hear the sincerity in Menno's voice, and knew he hated to disappoint her. But how had he managed to forget something so important? He shouldn't have been thinking of other things — like joining his friends in play. Flor shook her head. "Okay. Now go."

Menno slipped off the bed and ran to the construction site.

Flor watched him dart away and then left for her kitchen duties, still fuming at the carelessness of her seven-year-old but concerned for his safety. She had warned her children not to go there, yet it was hard for Pier and Menno to resist. It meant isolating themselves from the others. Besides, Pier had become fascinated with the construction process and studied the men as they worked. Menno enjoyed digging in the dirt and making his own buildings out of mud.

Just before noon, two Japanese soldiers guarding the entrance to Camp Ambarawa opened its arched metal gate to admit a local lorry piled high with wooden beams. A grouchy Indies driver nodded to the soldier, then lurched the old vehicle forward. Sitting cramped next to him were three snoozing Indies workers tasked with building the new barrack.

The truck rolled to a stop near the construction area, where close to one hundred fair-haired boisterous children dashed about yelling with glee. With no school, or planned activities, the site had become their playground. Some stopped to watch the workers unload and stack the heavy planks.

Pier, fluent in Malay, overheard a conversation between two construction workers.

One wearing a straw hat resembling an upside-down bucket sounded annoyed. *"Anak-anak orang Belanda menggangu saja. Mereka ada di mana-mana* [Dutch children are a nuisance. They're everywhere]!"

The other, slightly taller with a broad nose, glanced at his coworker. His deep-set eyes narrowed. *"Saya tahu bagaimana caranya untuk melenyapkan mereka* [I know just how to get rid of them]."

Pier squinted as he scrutinized the construction workers. Their menacing tone made him uncomfortable.

11

THE HEAVENS OPENED

"Pier! Come help me dig!" Menno picked up a stick and offered it to his brother.

As the boys played in the dirt, several other children joined them. Soon the two Indies workers arrived shouldering a heavy support beam. Some of the children noticed the men and stood up. Others, including Pier, watched to see what the men would do. Menno, absorbed in his project, continued digging intently.

One of the workers glanced at the other and nodded. They took a few hasty steps into the midst of the children and released the beam. The children near Menno threw themselves out of the way while others shrieked and bolted in terror.

Pier remained standing, transfixed, as his little brother's body flattened under the weight of the falling beam.

"Mennnnooooooooo!" Panic-stricken, Pier rushed to help him.

At the other end of the camp Flor glanced at the sky. It was her daily routine to return to the barrack from kitchen duty during her noon break, and it had suddenly become cloudy and overcast. But it didn't look like rain, so she could still take the little ones, Jantine and Ineke, for a brief mid-day walk. They needed her, and she longed for them. They were upset with the upheaval of their lives — the strange people, the new surroundings, the noise, and now her absence.

Holding hands, they walked in the garden behind the camp hospital to enjoy the bushes in early bloom. The girls clung tightly to their mother, finding comfort in her care.

Suddenly Flor heard someone scream, "*Mevrouw* Giliam, come quickly! Come quickly!" She looked up to see a woman running toward her waving frantically. "A terrible accident has happened!"

Flor froze.

"Menno's head!" the woman cried, her eyes filled with terror. From the direction of the construction site, Flor heard screaming. A voice shrieked, "They dropped a beam on him!"

Her heart racing, she let go of her daughters' hands and with slow strides advanced toward a group of children huddled together. Her legs felt like lead. She couldn't move them any faster. Then she saw Menno and stopped. He staggered a few steps, called, "Mama. Mama," and collapsed on the ground.

Her world began to spiral out of focus. Strength and courage drained from her body. Her beautiful cherub-like child needed her, but she couldn't move.

Flor watched from where she stood, as two women bent over Menno and carefully picked him up. Together they carried him into the ward where she and the children lived and laid him on a bed. Her children followed close behind.

Little Menno needed his mother, but the horror of seeing her son's skull crushed paralyzed her. She could only watch from a distance.

A long time passed before she could move. Slowly she crept toward the bed. The women and children surrounding Menno parted before her.

"Ma ... mmmm ... " she heard him whimper softly. But by the time she reached him, he was gone.

Flor's eyes filled with tears. Her precious, perfectly lovely boy with blond curls and sparkly bright blue eyes — a child who only spread joy and kindness — was dead. Flor's body went limp, her strength drained from her. Finally, she stooped and brushed her hand against his blond curls. Never again would she be able to hug Menno. Never again could she tell him how much she loved him. Menno was gone for good.

Flor instantly became consumed with doubt. Where was he now? She had not been able to talk to him much about death and heaven. What did Menno know? Had he asked Jesus to forgive him of his sins? Was he now with God in heaven? How would she ever know?

Two male Indies hospital workers, dressed in white tunics, entered to take Menno's lifeless body to St. Anthony's hospital in the nearby town of Ambarawa, and the small group of mourners dispersed.

How odd, thought Flor. Little Menno had come into the world in Sneek, Friesland, at a hospital also coincidentally named St. Anthony's when the family had been on furlough in May 1935. The happy event was still so fresh in her mind. How could his life be over so soon? How would she tell Menno that his precious son — his namesake — was gone?

Flor sat on the edge of her bunk grieving. Her body trembled violently. *I must remain strong for the children,* she told herself as she held back tears. Just then a comforting thought entered her mind. She summoned all her strength to call the children to herself. "Let's spend some time with the Lord now," she said.

She opened their little daily devotional called *A Grain of Wheat* and read the verse of the day for January 11. Taken from Matthew 3:16, the passage read, "And see, the heavens opened!" The precise words Flor needed to hear! God had spoken into her heart, *Heaven has received your son. He is now with me.* That wonderful promise made her burden so much easier to bear.

"Mama, where is Menno?" asked Hilda, in a tiny, confused voice.

"He is in heaven," she replied calmly, still trembling.

Pier, who had stayed by Flor's side from the time he left the construction site, couldn't contain his grief. "Menno is not in heaven! He is not dead!" he insisted, pulling on her arm. "Mama, don't bury him! I know for sure he's not dead!" he cried in desperation. "Mama don't! Please don't!"

Flor looked into Pier's sincere, pleading face and realized he really believed what he was saying. She had to help him understand, but what could she do to convince him? It hurt her to see Pier's pain. "Pier, *lieve schat.* Menno is not with us anymore."

"NO! NO!" Pier shouted outraged. He jumped to his feet and cried in defiance, "He's not dead! NO!"

"Quiet, Pier. Quiet," Flor gently took hold of his wrists and pulled him close, comforting him through her own tears. She held him tightly and lovingly stroked his back. The eleven-year-old melted into her embrace and wept bitterly, refusing to believe his little brother and best friend was gone. Forever.

～

WORD OF THE ACCIDENT SPREAD QUICKLY. TWO NUNS WHO HAD worked as nurses at the mission hospital offered to help Flor. They secured permission from the Japanese overseers at St. Anthony's hospital for Flor and Pier to visit the hospital morgue early the next morning.

When mother and son arrived, they found Menno lying on a narrow stone slab. He looked normal — serene and peaceful, except for a huge bruise on the side of his head from his temple to the back of his neck. Flor eyed Pier. With his head downcast, he stood next to her, limp and silent.

"Pier," she urged, "touch him."

The eleven-year-old took a deep breath and looked at his mother through grief-filled eyes.

"Go on ... " she said, encouraging him.

Reluctantly Pier reached out and touched his brother's hand, withdrawing it quickly.

"He's cold. Isn't he?"

Pier nodded.

"He isn't in his body anymore. He's with Jesus," Flor's voice was calm yet shaky. This would be the last time she would see her precious boy in this life, she reckoned. The pain was unbearable.

She turned away. "Pier," she asked softly, "do you understand now?"

Pier couldn't speak. He could only nod as tears streamed down his face.

Heartbroken, mother and son turned to leave. In silence, they walked back to the camp to prepare for Menno's burial later that day.

Unexpectedly, Flor was given one more opportunity to see Menno. When she returned to the morgue in the afternoon, she found him in a flimsy wooden coffin. Soon afterward, two male hospital attendants entered carrying a thin wooden lid. As they laid it into position, Menno's sweet face disappeared. Flor cringed. She knew she would never see her precious child again. How could life be so cruel and out of control?

Her body jolted, blow after blow, as the attendant hammered down the nails of the tiny coffin lid securing it in place. The sheer force and violence shook her core.

Outside the hospital, Yelly and Hilda had arrived neatly dressed. They were accompanied by the two nuns, who had also arranged for the reverends van der Berg and Kijlstra to officiate the burial. Heart-broken himself, Reverend Kijlstra knelt by Yelly's side and looked into her sorrowful blue eyes. Tenderly he wiped away her tears.

The attendants emerged from the hospital carrying the little coffin and placed it onto a crude, horse-drawn wagon. As it rolled away, Flor and Pier followed hand in hand.

"Flor ... " came the familiar deep voice of Reverend Kijlstra.

The unexpected presence of the two missionary pastors brought her great comfort. Flor's face lit up as she greeted both men with a gentle kiss on each check. *"Zo fijn om u hier te zien. Dankuwel voor uw komst* [So good to see you. Thank you for coming]."

Reverend Kijlstra's eyes were full of grief. *"Het ... spijt me zo* [I'm ... so sorry]."

The small procession passed outside the camp gate onto the road to the cemetery, the tiny coffin shifting precariously as the cart wobbled along the crude road spotted with murky, water-filled potholes. A quiet Indies youth did his best to guide the horse around them on its brief twenty-minute journey to the cemetery.

The mourners, accompanied by a sympathetic Japanese guard, followed the slain child. Dozens of teary, interned women watched through the barbwire fence as the coffin passed by. Mieke stood among them, wiping tears that spilled down her cheeks. Spontaneously she began singing a familiar hymn — one Flor loved. Others joined in:

> *Daar ruischt langs de wolken een lief'lijke Naam,*
> *Die hemel en aarde vereenigt te zaam.*

Geen naam is er zoeter en beter voor 't hart,
Hij balsemt de wonden en heelt alle smart.
Kent gij, kent gij dien Naam nog niet?
Dien naam draagt mijn Heiland, mijn lust en mijn lied!

[Far above the clouds I hear the sound of a
 lovely name
Uniting heaven and earth together again.
No name is more lovely and better for the heart.
He balms the wounds and heals all sadness.
Do you, do you know that name as yet?
It's the name of Jesus, my Savior, my joy and my
 song!]

Even in her sadness Flor acknowledged her sympathetic compatriots with a kind nod. Her thoughts drifted back to the little service held earlier in the day at the camp. It was led by Lillian Hooysma, who had prepared the eulogy.

She had pointed out Menno's special qualities in his interactions with others and his favorable disposition. Flor remembered those words, but the rest of the service became a blur. Her grief was overwhelming.

The somber group arrived at the cemetery hill and gathered under the shade of a magnificent Indies tree. Menno's tiny coffin was in front of them on a heap of dirt surrounded by lush, unkept grass.

The minister pulled a pocket Bible from his white suit jacket and opened it to Matthew 3:16. He read: "And when Jesus was baptized, immediately he went up from the water, and behold, the heavens were opened to him, and he saw the Spirit of God descending like a dove and coming to rest on him; and behold, a voice from heaven said … "

He stopped momentarily waiting for his emotions to settle, then resumed slowly, measuring his words: "This is my beloved Son, with whom I am well pleased."

Flor closed her eyes. *My beloved son with whom I am well pleased.* Tears meandered down her cheeks.

Reverend Kijlstra continued in a soft voice, his words echoing the message given earlier by *Mevrouw* Hooysma. "When night comes and the storm rages, faith shows the true force of its power — hope. Our child is now in the loving arms of our heavenly Father."

"Papa," Flor heard Pier whisper. She looked at him staring at the casket. The full weight of the loss of his little brother was settling on him. Flor could see how much he needed the strength and comfort of his father.

The reverend tucked the well-worn book back into his suit pocket. "Don't be ashamed of your tears," he added. "You do well to bring your burdens to the Lord. Only He can deliver you." He concluded the service with a chorus.

> *Daar boven juicht een grote schaar*
> *Van kindren voor God's troon*
> *Verlost van zonden van gevaar,*
> *Tot eer van's Vader's Zoon*

> [High in the sky is a tremendous throng
> Of children before God's throne
> Delivered from sin and danger,
> To the honor of the Father's Son]

Like a soothing balm, the familiar words reassured Flor's aching soul. This was Menno's favorite hymn — the one they had often sung together as a family. In her mind's eye, Flor could see her precious boy singing wholeheartedly with the other children before God's throne. Her little Menno was now with his heavenly Father. She would never doubt it again.

> *Hoe kwamen z'in in dat heerlijk oord?*
> *Zij hoorden Jezus' stem,*

Geloofden in zijn dierbaar woord
En gaven 't hart aan Hem.

[How did they get in this wonderful place?
They heard Jesus' voice,
Believed in his precious word
And gave their heart to Him.]

The young Japanese escort's eyes were soft. He was visibly touched by the burial of the little boy and he followed the procession back to the camp respectfully.

As the group approached the entrance gate, the minister leaned toward Flor and lowered his voice. "Unfortunately, I have some more bad news," he said gently.

Flor felt a rush of alarm. She turned to him with pleading eyes. "Reverend, you're not going to tell me something terrible has happened to my husband!"

"Oh, no! No!" he assured her. "It's not about Menno. It's your home — the mission. Everything is gone. Stolen."

Flor stopped abruptly and peered at him with pained eyes. "Reverend Kijlstra, I have just buried my son. What else could possibly matter?"

Flor's thoughts now focused on her children. They needed her, especially Pier. He looked so lost without his little brother.

The procession continued toward the camp gate in silence. Flor's reality seemed strange and altered. How could people carry on with banal activities when, for her, life had stopped?

As she approached the barrack, Mieke ran to embrace her with open arms. All the women shared in the loss of young Menno — the first child to die in the camp — as if he were their own son. A female doctor asked if she could do anything to help.

"Jantine's completely dehydrated," Mieke responded swiftly. "Please do something for the little one. I fear for her life!"

Since they'd arrived in Ambarawa, the two-year-old had not been eating or drinking enough. She thrived on love and routine, but the war had turned her life upside down. Worse yet, she remained unsupervised with the other children each day when Flor attended to her work duties. The upheaval had disrupted the toddler physically and emotionally.

Flor cared a great deal about Jantine and tried to think, but her mind was numb.

Immediately, the doctor arranged for Flor to bring Jantine to the camp hospital. For the third time that day, Flor found herself returning there, this time with Jantine riding in the *slendang* — a cloth carrier on her back. It was a difficult journey.

When Flor learned Jantine would have to remain in the hospital for a few days, she despaired. The place immediately filled her mind with images of Menno's little body. It was still so raw. How could she now leave her precious toddler there alone? Flor had to force herself to believe the hospital would help her little one live. With loving care and rest in a crib like the one in Gombong, Jantine would recover.

In the days that followed, the women in the camp were given the opportunity to send a postcard message to their husbands. How Flor longed to share her grief with Menno, but she was forbidden to speak of young Menno's death. Though disappointed, she reasoned the men probably had enough hardships of their own. In the end it didn't matter, the postcards were never delivered.

∼

LOCATION UNKNOWN, JAVA

January 12, 1943

My darling Flor, last night I dreamed about you, and about how I would love to be near you and near my children. I carry you always in my thoughts, day and night.

It was just announced that we will be leaving here the night of January 13th, at midnight. We still haven't heard what our destination will be. However, it seems increasingly likely that the trip will lead us overseas after all. We've also received notice that Dutch money will have to be exchanged for Japanese. That's when the rumors about us being shipped overseas increased — though I still refuse to believe it. I hope and pray the Lord will save us from this awful plan. I stubbornly hope to be home again soon.

Tomorrow night we'll have to walk at least 15 kilometers with our luggage. It will make no difference whether one is sick or not. It will be hell for many. Kees Hartman, for instance, came down with a high fever. It means he could have typhus, but he'll have to walk the distance regardless. For me, it will be no problem. The Lord has kept me well so far.

You probably will not hear from me until we've arrived at our destination. We are all tremendously anxious as to where we will be going. I realize that whether we are sent home or transported to Japan, the Lord will go with us.

Funny but right now I'm imagining the day when we'll be together again and ... we will read all these lines I have written to you. Then it will be all behind us.

My dear ones, I'm committing you into God's faithful care and protection. Bye for now, dearest Flor. And how are you dear Yell [Yelly] and how about you, Pjirk [Pier] and my dear Phil [Hilda] and Menno, sweet little Ann [Anneke], dear Ina [Ineke], and my darling little Janny [Jantine]?

Much love from your loving father, Menno.

PHOTOS

Florence Giliam with her children prior to Internment, 1942. Centre: Florence,
Clock-wise behind Florence: Jelly (pronounced Yelly), Pier, Menno Jr., Anneke,
Jantine, Ineke, Hilda.

Ambarawa Japanese Internment Camp Seven. [3]

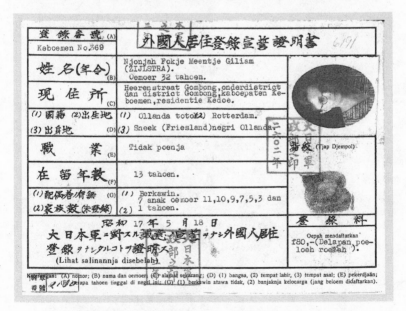

Florence Giliam's Japanese occupation ID card.

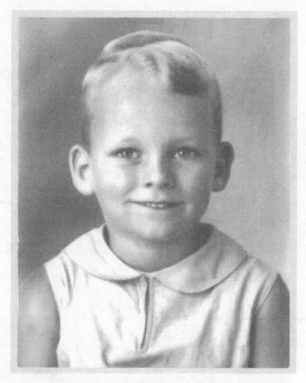

Menno Anne Giliam

Women and Children Japanese Internment Camp: Washing
Station [3]

Women and Children Japanese Internment Camp: Women bowing at roll call.
[3]

Women and Children Japanese Internment Camp, Java [3]

CAGED ANIMALS

Tanjung Priok, North Java, January 13, 1943

Hundreds of Dutch POWs stood waiting on the bustling Tanjung Priok dock in North Jakarta. Along the edge of the barnacle-encrusted concrete piers, thick ropes and oversized metal chains secured the docked military and cargo ships. It was early morning, January 13, 1943, and the exhausted men had just arrived from an overnight journey by foot. A foghorn issued a sudden low, drawn-out wail as white tufts rose from the charred smokestacks of a Japanese-flagged steamship.

Among the POWs stood Menno, de Graaf and de Wit. The men felt uneasy. Menno studied the expanse of the vessel and pondered its destination. Where would they be shipped? The Japanese intentionally withheld this information to try to break their spirits.

One thing was certain: they were leaving their families behind. Were Flor and the children still in Gombong, or elsewhere on the island? How Menno wished he could be there to protect them.

Suddenly, chaos broke out. Shouting Japanese guards issued a tirade of staccato commands, rifles held high for reinforcement.

Go this way; that way; up the stairs; then down. No one knew where they were to go.

The line of bewildered POWs snaked toward the ship and struggled up the rusty gang plank, slippery from overuse and moisture.

"*Isoge! Motto hayaku ugoke* [Hurry up! Move faster]!" An aggressive Japanese soldier barked at a slow-moving POW, butting him with his rifle.

Menno hoped that once on board, a cool, salty sea breeze might revive the exhausted men. Instead, they were directed through a narrow trap door, down a ladder into the ship's hold. As Menno's eyes adjusted to the dimly lit compartment, he saw handmade, boarded bunks stacked one above the other, built into the musty chamber. *They've really gone out of their way to prepare for us. They've built cages*, he thought. A Japanese soldier, staring down the barrel of his rifle, pointed each man to his bunk. Menno climbed into his cage of bare planks and looked down. De Graaf, de Wit and the others were disappearing like rabbits behind the boards.

"Traveling in style! Courtesy of Japan," piped de Graaf, his bunk just below Menno's.

"Wonder what's on the menu?" retorted the Frisian with like sarcasm.

Wit lay on his wooden plank staring at the bunks of the two above. He snapped his fingers. "Bartender! Heineken ... over here!"

"Make that three!" quipped de Graaf.

The men laughed and enjoyed a moment of respite, yet fear gnawed at them as much as hunger.

It soon became apparent to the POWs that the inhumane transport tagged the "hell ship" was a floating target for the allies.

For three days and nights the Dutch POWs sailed in the belly of the ship feeling tired, dirty, seasick, and nauseous from the stench. *I know how Jonah must have felt,* thought Menno, yet in his bunk he found a place of solitude. From his leather canteen he retrieved a scrap of notepaper, and from his pocket, the pencil — a stolen moment to write a note to Flor.

∽

TANJUNG PRIOK PORT, JAVA

January 14, 1943

When I looked down from my bed, it suddenly dawned on me that we had become mere animals. Everywhere men were disappearing behind a board like rabbits in a cage. For a moment, it almost seemed funny ... but then a feeling of great loneliness swept over me. There we were, completely exhausted from the trip with strangers all around us.

The boat was in its final boarding procedures and it was not long before we set sail. It had become pitch black in the hull and before I realized it, I was sound asleep. The next morning, I discovered that one of my few belongings, a jar of peanut butter, had been stolen. We were on our way to Singapore.

∽

PANDEMONIUM ACCOMPANIED ALL JAPANESE BOARDING, LOADING and debarkation of the POWs. Arrival into Singapore was no exception. Loud, irate Japanese soldiers shoved the unwashed, wretched men as they herded them from the ship. Unsteady from the journey at sea, they stumbled down the gangplank. Some buckled under the weight of their duffel bags, weak from malnourishment, or illness. Several carried a stretcher bearing the lifeless body of a comrade.

∽

POW CAMP, SINGAPORE

January 18, 1943

From Java, the transports arrive [in Singapore] and then continue on to Indochina and Japan. Already 86 Dutchmen have been buried here. An outbreak of dysentery took the lives of 38 of them. If it hadn't been for all of you — my heart aches and longs greatly for you always — I wouldn't have minded laying down my weary body to die here also. All I can think about is how are things with my loved ones?

Mijn schat, when I look at the picture of you and my seven little ones, my heart trembles with fear and despair. How hard is the road we have to travel — and this isn't even our final destination!

$\sim$

THE DUTCH POWS WERE GIVEN ONLY TWO DAYS IN THE CAMP, A former British army barracks, to recover from the grueling ocean voyage before the Japanese forced them to take on work duties. Each morning the men walked a great distance to a job site to excavate a parcel of land. The labor was exhausting, and the daily food rations minimal. Often a mere bowl of dry rice constituted a meal. Occasionally, tasteless soup enhanced by a local vegetable augmented their supper. Menno found the food revolting, yet to ward off starvation, he ate whatever was offered.

$\sim$

POW CAMP, SINGAPORE

January 18, 1943

Close to our camp is a huge prison full of English men, women and children!

When all these worries become too much, I think about our prayers constantly being sent up to the Lord Sabbaoth, as we cry for help, strength and forgiveness for all our trespasses.

My dear ones, if I didn't believe that in this life our faithful Shepherd and Redeemer would be the Lord, our God, where would our strength and protection come from? He will not hide His face forever but will have compassion on His repentant children. "Help us, Oh Lord. Give us confidence in You. Grant that we may love You with all our hearts. Increase our faith!

... Bye dear ones.

Your Menno.

∾

DESPITE THE PHYSICAL DEMANDS AND LACK OF SUSTENANCE, MENNO settled into his new routine and felt healthy. But it didn't last long. Soon word came the POWs would be moving to another undisclosed location.

∾

JANUARY 20, 1943

Mijn schatjes,

Today, it was announced that this coming Monday we will be leaving again, destination unknown. Undoubtedly, it will be a long journey, but you know I've been greatly encouraged by the Lord. He has clearly shown me that He will go with us. I'm sure you have heard about all the transports that left Java. Flor, how your heart must have shrunk from fear and worry. I know just how you feel, darling.

All essential information is being kept from us, so as to slowly but surely break us. But what a difference it makes that we can bring all before our mighty Father. Imagine this life without Him. Our despair would have been all too real, for it is from Him that time and time again we receive new strength to carry on.

While we're waiting for our departure, I found some time to read a commentary on Psalm 27. It was just beautiful. It refreshed my soul and spirit, just as my mind is being refreshed by the beauty of nature here. There is hardly any precipitation right now and it is not too humid. It's just right. My health is excellent considering the meager diet. A blessing never to be appreciated enough.

I join Jacob [in the Bible] in saying, "If you, Lord, will go with me on the way and bring me back again to my wife and children, then, I will honor You all the days of my life and give You a tenth of all my first fruit."

... There is so much to be thankful for, even here. To make demands now is not fitting, now and never really was. Whatever I receive right now is unlimited grace.

Flor, just imagine for a minute what it will be like when we are together again! Mijn kleine schatjes [my little darlings] one little hug right now would mean so much. But who knows, maybe the illusive day of freedom is closer than we realize.

My roommate is Hans de Wit again. We enjoyed playing a game of chess this afternoon. It was great fun. A little while ago, we all had our supper. It consisted of rice with some wild jungle vegetation.

I must say, "Bye" for now.

Much love from your deeply loving Menno.

≈

JANUARY 21, 1943

Last night, we were able to attend a service in an English Church. Rev. Schaeffer chose the topic "Why worry about tomorrow?" Look at the birds and the lilies of the field. What a wonderful carefree life in God's Name. To be wonderfully free from worry — this is God's will for us. The only prerequisite is that we hand our lives over to Him.

Schat, I'm happy to tell you that this is just what I've done. I feel totally safe in the hands of the Lord. I'm not even worried about you. God will make it well. I believe that whole-heartedly. You must realize that though I'm still a part of this life, my soul goes out to the Living God from whom I expect everything ...

Rev. Schaeffer informed us that Bert van der Kouwe has been hospital-
ized. Hans de Wit and I hope to visit him as soon as possible. John
Kamerling from Semarang lays buried here at the local cemetery. Isn't
that horrible? Hopefully, we will be able to visit the grave someday, to
pay our respects. I vividly remember the times he and I went for walks
together at Wonosobo on the island of Java ...

∾

In Singapore, the church services brought Menno life-giving
moments of hope, as well as painful moments of deep retro-
spection.

At the front of the sanctuary, in the colonial English chapel, a
dozen skinny Dutch POWs in filthy shorts and shirts stood
singing the Dutch anthem. Menno glanced around the church
interior. The carefully handcrafted wooden benches contrasted
with the great holes in the walls. Gaping and jagged, they told of
violent gun battles in the not too distant past.

With sadness, he noted that while church services were available
to more than a thousand POWs, not many attended. *Why so few?*
he wondered. *Would there be more if believers had allowed Jesus to*
show His love through their words and deeds?

The sound of the male voices singing the second stanza of the
anthem bounced majestically between the chapel walls:

> *Mijn schild ende betrouwen,*
> *Zijt Gij, O God mijn Heer.*
> *Op U zo wil ik bouwen,*
> *Verlaat mij nimmermeer ...*

> [My shield and my fortress
> Art Thou, O Lord my God.
> It is you on whom I build my hope,
> Never leave me nor forsake me ...]

Memories of his family flooded Menno's mind. Agony gripped his soul and his thoughts tormented him. *Mijn kleine lieve schatjes* [My little lovely darlings], *the way your papa treated you was often so harsh. God, have mercy on me!*

As the prisoners finished the last stanza of the anthem, he buried his face in his hands and wept.

> *Dat ik doch vroom mag blijven,*
> *uw dienaar t'aller stond,*
> *en de tirannie verdrijven*
> *die mijn hart doorwondt.*

> [Grant that I may remain
> a brave servant of yours for always,
> and drive away the tyranny
> that tries my heart.]

∽

JANUARY 24, 1943

This morning I attended the church service, again ... But don't think we have nothing to do here on Sundays. We work as usual, but at least we get a chance to attend the church service ...

Rev. Schaeffer spoke about the fact that the world and all that is in it, is the Lord's. It wasn't really a sermon, just a word from his heart to ours. We'll soon leave here and Rev. Schaeffer, who's been with us all this time, will stay behind. He was really moved.

One of the men, whom he had baptized, briefly spoke a word of thanks as well. I felt deeply touched by it all. Again, a cold wave of loneliness and emptiness swept over me. It all seems so unreal — all that has happened to us in such a short time. At the moment, I feel utterly separated from all my loved ones. You, and yes, even my Heavenly Father!

... We don't hear anything about how the war is progressing. Who's winning? What's happening? We seem to be wasting away here. How

long will it continue? Yet I know that we are in God's hands and we will find mercy in His eyes, even today. This prayer is especially for you and the children: that He may comfort and help you. Do the little ones beg for food from you and are you able to give it to them? "Help us Oh Lord, because of Your lovingkindness."

My dear ones, a nice big hug for you all. And Flor, put your trust in God. He will supply your needs, my love.

Bye for now, from your sorrowful, longing and hoping husband, Menno.

~

AMBARAWA CAMP 7, EARLY 1943

The harsh glare from the outdoor spotlights flooding the camp grounds pierced through the paint-chipped window shutters illuminating more than a hundred women and children lying on their bunks. It was past curfew, yet the crowded ward was awake.

The nightly symphony of grumbling stomachs had begun. A kind, weather-beaten Marjan lay quietly looking at the ceiling. Conversation about food had become a nightly obsession.

She mused, *"Ontbijtkoek smaakte hier altijd veel beter dan toen ik het in Holland maakte. Misschien omdat de kruiden frisser zijn. Dat denk ik* [Spice cake always tastes better here than when I made it in Holland. Maybe because the spices are fresher. That's what I think]."

The other women listened intently. A young woman eager to learn more turned over and propped herself on one elbow. *"Ja? Welke kruiden gebruikt u* [Yah? Which spices do you use]?"

"Gember, kaneel, kruidnagel. Maar het belangrijkste is kardemom. Verse kardemom [Ginger, cinnamon, cloves. But the most important is cardamom. Fresh cardamom]." Marjan's voice was wistful.

"Mmmmm! *Ik kan het nu al proven* [I can already taste it]!" replied the other, dropping back on her pillow with eyes shut and smiling.

Another young woman with tight, curly brown hair sat on the edge of her bed rocking her baby to sleep. "Do you know what I crave?" she asked. "Delicious potatoes from Holland, mashed with kale. *Ja, en met een grote rookworst, natuurlijk!* [Yes, and with a large smoked sausage, of course]!"

The women snickered. Mieke looked around to see if Ineke was still awake. She spotted the little girl sitting on her bed playing with her ragged doll. "Ineke come! Do you have a story for us?"

Five-year-old Ineke's eyes were heavy and tired, set in ever-deepening circles. Her nightdress hung loosely from her tiny, malnourished body. Though her belly ached relentlessly, the quiet, serious child was always eager to tell stories, and she was good at it. She slipped off her bed and zipped across to Mieke's bunk. She took a moment to collect her thoughts and then began, earnestly, with her brow furrowed.

"This story is about a *kleine jongetje* [small boy], *Jantje Tomaat* [Johnny Tomato]."

The women chuckled. Ineke was animated and engaging.

"He lived in the camp with his mother. One day she couldn't work in the fields anymore because she was very sick. And she was very sad. So *Jantje* planted her a beautiful tomato garden."

"Where did he get the seeds?" a woman called from a bunk.

"Hmmm." Ineke paused a moment. "He took them from his father's garden in Gombong. He kept them in his pocket."

A woman coughed in the background, and a child cried. Another woman rocked her tiny baby to sleep, yet the women nearby listened intently. They found the animated little girl immensely entertaining.

Ineke stretched her arm as high above her head as she could reach. "The tomato plant grew and grew and grew. So tall!"

She mimed a huge tomato, the size of a melon, with her hands.

"And a big fat tomato grew and grew and grew. But then, suddenly a Jap came. Oh no! *Jantje* had to hide his big tomato, or the Jap would hit him and take it away. Could *Jantje* put it in his pocket?"

Ineke shook her little finger. "No! His pocket had big holes. Could he hide it under his shirt? No! Because everyone would think he was having a baby." Ineke stuck out her stomach, pretending to be pregnant. The women cackled.

She became serious again. "So *Jantje* put it in his mouth!"

Her eyes grew wide as she mimicked a small boy fitting a big round tomato in his mouth. She puffed out her cheeks and attempted to speak, but the words were inaudible. Ineke looked up at the imaginary Jap, and with palms up and hands raised, shrugged her shoulders. The women laughed. Flor shook her head and smiled. She, too, was amused.

"The Jap went away. Peh!" Ineke spat out the imaginary tomato and held it up in her two hands.

"*Hoera* [Hooray]! *Jantje* brought the tomato home to his mother. She ate it and got all better!"

Ineke ran and flopped on her mother's bed. Though weak and tired, the women clapped and cheered. The tiny, fair-haired five-year-old had given the ward momentary relief from their misery.

∾

JANUARY 25, 1943

Yesterday, Ben Oozinga paid me a visit. Of course, I immediately asked him if he knew anything about you and the children. He thought you had moved to Keboeman in Brinkman's house. I do hope that it's true.

You would be close to the hospital and nurses. Ben also lent me $2.50.
What a great guy! I'm going to buy something really special when I get
a chance.

This morning I saw a doctor. I'm suffering from diarrhea and my legs
feel like lead. He prescribed a couple of days rest. However, that will be
short-lived for this coming Wednesday we will be leaving camp and
will travel northward. That promises to be a tough day. I, for one, am
glad we're leaving here, for the food, especially, leaves a lot to be
desired. We are being starved to death. Hopefully, things will be better
in [Thailand].

If only I knew the Lord a little closer. He seems so far away. I must
confess though, time and again, I am the one who turns away from
Him. Don't we always? Our thoughts crowd Him out. This thought
pattern has to change. I catch myself constantly thinking things that I
know are not pleasing Him. It is so hard. When will this change? God
be merciful to me!

∾

SINGAPORE TRAIN STATION, JANUARY 26, 1943

The Dutch POWs crowded inside the Japanese truck braced
themselves as it sputtered and lurched forward. Departing from
Singapore's train station, many were relieved to say good-bye to
the unrelenting field labor and the uncomfortable living quarters, but what lay ahead? Menno had mixed feelings. Rumor had
it they were being sent deeper into the interior of Indochina,
further from home.

Thirty kilometers later the male cargo disembarked at Changi
Train Station, Singapore, where a twenty-five-car freight train
waited for them. Each wagon measured only six by two meters,
and the Japanese packed the men in like cattle. With the midday
sun bearing down on them, the inside of the cars quickly turned
into sweltering ovens.

Menno stood crammed together with twenty-seven other POWs, with no bench to sit on, nor adequate ventilation. Two men in a corner soon collapsed, ill with dysentery and diarrhea. Others sat on the floor in spite of the filth and human excrement. For four long days and nights their reeking, sweating bodies jostled against each other as the train rocked and lurched its way northward. The stench was unbearable.

Thin streaks of light flashed through slits in the rail car walls illuminating the bodies of the tortured occupants. Once a day the rusty, brown locomotive screeched to a jarring halt. Loud, yelling Japanese soldiers routinely appeared, unlatched the heavy, barred iron doors and swung them open. Weak and dehydrated, two dozen emaciated Dutch POWs floundered out, squinting at the bright sunlight.

Some immediately collapsed on the lush, green, grassy field. Others hurried to relieve themselves. Menno wandered alongside the track, snatching up blades of grass. He quickly shoved the vegetation into his mouth and began to chew. No. Not bitter. He continued eating voraciously.

Two POWs emerged from the train carrying the lifeless body of a friend. Not all survived the ordeal.

~

UNKNOWN LOCATION IN NORTH WESTERN THAILAND

February 2, 1943

Mijn schatjes,

It has been over a week since I last wrote to you. I have some time right now, so let me tell you what has happened ...

When we finally got off the train, we continued traveling by truck. This trip was at least as bad as the one before. The roads where the trucks had to maneuver through were almost non-existent. During our train ride, we had hardly eaten and now our menu called for rotten fish. Finally, on January 31, we arrived at a temporary base.

Here, we experienced our first camp under the stars. We were driven together like a herd and there we slept in a corral, just like animals. But still, I was in good health, though extremely weary. I slept like a baby. Early in the morning, I awakened with thousands of stars twinkling above my head. I was reminded of Jacob and how he had slept under the stars while he was in deep trouble at Bethel.

Soon we had to move on again. We gathered our few belongings and started out on a two-hour walk. A truck carried us further into the jungle ...

∽

THE ARDUOUS JOURNEY INTO THE DEEP JUNGLE BROUGHT AN unexpected gift — a fresh, clear stream. It had been a long time since the men drank pure water. "It tastes sublime," yelled one. They bathed in it, washed their clothes and felt tremendously refreshed.

During the second night rain fell and the POWs awoke in a dense fog. As a result, the Japanese leaders announced they could rest another day, a much-needed respite.

The men then walked for several days through rugged terrain to arrive at a railway construction camp. Word quickly spread that the Japanese were using POWs and civilian prisoners as slave labor to lay tracks to link existing railways so they would have a direct line from Bangkok, Thailand, to Rangoon, Burma.

The following day the men gathered their belongings and walked for two more hours to trucks that carried them further into the jungle.

On the fourth day, they hiked twenty kilometers across mountainous terrain to their destination, Rintin, one of the many railway construction camps that held one thousand prisoners. The men were so starved, thirsty and desperate, they drank almost anything. Before the journey ended, they buried another comrade.

~

FEBRUARY 2ND, 1943

Flor ... Our lives are in constant danger with sickness, accidents and trouble everywhere ...

Only our Heavenly Father has the power to keep me going, or to deliver me to Himself. My one fervent hope in life is to see you all again.

~

BY THE FIFTH OF FEBRUARY, THE DUTCH POWs SETTLED INTO Rintin. Railroad construction began immediately.

13

RAILWAY OF DEATH

MENNO STOPPED TO LISTEN. THE SOUND OF FOREST INSECTS, JUNGLE birds, and the nearby mountain stream synchronized into one noisy discord. How his world had changed since he left the serene landscape of his native Friesland fifteen years earlier! He could never have imagined himself in a place like this when he dedicated his life to serve God.

On his return from a long day of work on the railroad, he wandered into the forest to seek a hideaway. Not far from the path leading to the river, he spotted it — a mammoth Thai forest fig. The three-foot-high above-ground roots extended for several meters from its base, grasping the ground like giant claws. *Perfect cover,* he thought.

Considerably leaner, and marked with cuts and bruises, he wedged himself between two massive root folds, invisible to passers-by. He withdrew a pencil from his pant pocket and notepaper from his canteen. Where to begin? He rubbed his bristly, unshaven chin as he considered what to write. *February 5th, 1943 ...* he began.

An annoying mosquito momentarily stole his attention. He stopped writing to swat the insect and peer through the underbrush at a group of POWs stumbling back to base camp from bathing in the river. Malnourished and thin, the men faltered in their effort to carry heavy buckets of water to their thatched-roof barracks. They spent every spare moment acquiring water to boil for drinking.

When the POWs disappeared down the path under the lengthening shadows, Menno resumed his contemplation and letter writing.

Upon arrival, Captain Althing van Geuso called us for a brief address. His message can be summarized with these words: "The Japs brought us here to annihilate us, so my advice is look after yourselves!" But I couldn't help but think, "There is still someone who looks after us — the Lord!"

The Captain's warning proved true. Death loomed over the railway construction and reigned at camp Rintin. Workers were subject to extreme Japanese cruelty and were forced to work under torturous conditions with inadequate tools, poor treatment, starvation and illness.

The Emperor of Japan had allotted fifteen months — an unreasonably short time — for building a railway intended to aid their war effort. An estimated three hundred thirty thousand men formed the construction crews, including sixty-one thousand Australian, British, Dutch and American prisoners of war, and unfortunate Malay and Burmese citizens deceived, or rounded up to work as laborers. An estimated thirty percent died during construction.

A section of the railway was built along the Khwae Noi River — the notorious waterway popularized by the movie, *The Bridge on the River Kwai*. The time Menno spent at this location from mid-February until October 1943 was considered the worst and most difficult period of construction.

Labor on the railway was hazardous, and the conditions extreme. Tracks were often required to meander around towering sheer rock cliffs at dizzying heights. The lattice structures of wooden beams supporting the train tracks seemed precarious at best.

Lack of nutrition reduced POWs to walking skeletons. Many labored bare-chested and in shorts. Others wore only black loincloths because their garments had been reduced to threads. Barefoot, or in well-worn shoes or boots, the emaciated Dutchmen toiled in the scorching sun under the watchful eyes of the Japanese guards.

With hands that betrayed hard labor, and nails cracked and soiled, Menno fingered a loose scrap of paper and wedged himself further into the folds of the fig tree. A slight smirk lit up his countenance as he recalled the previous day's events.

We had put up camp near a river again. Yesterday, I swam across the swiftly streaming current ... Willem de Graaf and I were wading about when he decided to swim across. I immediately decided to follow him. We quickly realized that the current was much stronger and the river much wider than we had anticipated. For a moment, I feared that we would not make it. Fortunately, we reached the shore safely. No sooner had we set foot on land, we heard a Jap yelling at us to come back immediately, while aiming his gun at us. Needless to say, we had no choice but to get back as fast as we could. Still swimming beside Graaf, I reached shore safely once more.

Last night, we slept outside again. Two more nights in a row under the stars. The days are extremely hot, but at night, especially in the early morning hours, it is quite cold. In spite of this, I have slept really well from about eleven at night until seven in the morning. If the food remains the same, we'll lose even more weight.

I sometimes wonder how long we will be able to hold out. It's rumored that we will move further north, deeper into the interior of Thailand, and even closer to China. In the meantime, God is the one who cares for you and to Him be the glory and honor forever.

Bye schatjes. Love from your deeply loving husband, Menno.

~

February 7, 1943

Today is a pretty miserable Sunday. The barracks are being inspected by the Japs. We work as usual in this relentless heat. The food is still horrible. I have problems swallowing it.

Flor, how I would love to have a cup of coffee or dinner with you — just once. Now, we simply eat whatever is in front of us to stay alive. We don't ask for anything.

Flor, our path isn't easy. It's a hard and rough road, just like the Israelites under Pharaoh in Egypt — hard labor and merciless oppression. If God doesn't shorten the time and if He doesn't sustain us moment by moment, then we will not last much longer. To be so far from home and from all my loved ones this Sunday is more than I can bear. "Lord, bring us back together again soon."

To my little darlings and you Flor, be strong. Kleine schatjes, pray to God for mercy. Your loving husband and dad, Menno.

Sunburned and dripping sweat, Menno lifted a hammer high above his head. With a few swift blows, he drove a metal spike into a rail tie. Nearby, a Japanese engineer with round, metal-framed glasses yelled at a tall, broad-shouldered POW hoisting a beam with a primitive pulley.

Loose stones from the rock face bounced off the support beam where Menno stood, before free-falling to the canyon below. Menno paused in the hot sun to wipe his brow with the back of his arm and reached for his canteen.

Long days of heavy labor compounded by inhumane working conditions took their toll on the POWs deep in the jungles of northern Thailand. Few recovered, if infested with intestinal parasites, or after contracting dysentery. Both were rampant in the POW camps. Once sick, they received little care or mercy from their Japanese captors.

February 17, 1943

Schatjes,

... you've constantly been on my mind ... You probably know a lot more about what's happening at the frontiers than we do here, deep in the [Thai] jungle. At the moment, I'm not feeling all that well. I guess I've caught a cold. Little wonder really since at night it's so cold that we have trouble falling asleep. Our feet are especially icy cold. Probably this diet is having some effect on our circulation.

In the morning hours, we are awakened by the cries of hundreds of apes, which live in the trees around us. I bet they are freezing too! This is followed by hard work, as usual, the cutting of trees and the laying of tracks during the day. We are like slaves building the railroad that will lead from [Thailand] to Burma. The workload is so heavy that by the end of the day, we are exhausted! After this, we still have to boil our water for the next day.

I shouldn't be complaining. In the midst of all the pain and sorrow, there are still countless blessings and balm for our wounds ...

... Last night, a Japanese boy brought me a piece of cake, five bananas and a box of cigars. Thanks be to the Lord. I felt just like Elijah at the brook, where the ravens brought him food. The boy wants to be my friend, he says. His name is Kondo. He will try to buy a few more things.

My dearest ones, bye for now. Love from your husband and dad, Menno.

∼

FEBRUARY 22, 1943

I'll quickly throw out a lifeline. How are you all? God, our God, is taking care of you, that I know. He is such a faithful, good Father. He keeps me also from day to day.

My only problem right now is a throat infection, but I prefer that to intestinal problems, which often lead to complications. Just about everyone here has had swollen lips and an infected throat because of the dust. These infections come and go, but not so for the patients suffering from dysentery. There are hundreds right now, many of them seriously ill. Every night, the sound of the Last Post [signaling the death of another POW] echoes through the camp. It encourages me to be able to render a service to those that are sick. Tomorrow, it may be too late. It's such a pleasure to give them something, like a broth, some bananas or sometimes an egg. Of course, those little luxuries are expensive, but at least now we have a chance to buy from the Thais outside the camp — which is considered smuggling and very dangerous.

Dearest Flor, I'm really experiencing God's forgiving grace, help and favor in this life, just like He promised all through His Word. Flor, I tell you, it is a tremendous privilege!

Menno regularly sought comfort from Scripture, his favorite being Psalm 91. He considered each word carefully using precious paper and time to write it out.

He who dwells in the shelter of the Most High
will abide in the shadow of the Almighty.

I will say to the Lord, "My refuge and my fortress,
my God, in whom I trust."

How pitiful this existence would be if I had to do without His loving protection …

Last night, all the Christians here came together, Catholics and Protestants. Funny, once you end up in circumstances like these, you forget to bicker about different points of view. Together we sought the face of the Lord and found forgiveness and grace.

Flor, I would like to mention something. Whether or not we will see each other again on earth, I do not know. One thing I do know is that in heaven we will meet again, without sadness or sorrow or remorse. It will be in great joy, darling.

Take care of our little ones. Oh, that I would see you all again on this earth. "Grant it, Oh Lord, for your Name's sake, to praise you from generation to generation."

Again, bye for now. Love, Menno.

～

FEBRUARY 26, 1943

... Death literally stalks among us. Every day, people pass away. From the approximate one thousand POWs, three or four die every night without fail. That is why we hear the Last Post. It's just awful. Another seven hundred men are ill, some seriously.

Yet, it has pleased God to extend many favors towards me. I'm still able to walk around here. And though there is much affliction and suffering under these severe circumstances, I can look at these conditions in the security of being at peace with the Lord ... God has received me in spite of all my sins and everything else that caused me to turn away from Him. For this, I will thank Him forever ...

How are my little ones doing? Yel — pel ... dearest Yel [Yelly], my first-born child, a child born out of prayer. How are you doing? Are you helping mama? Dear, dear Pjirk [Pier], are you comforting your mother, my dearest big boy; and my sweet Phil [Hilda] and little Menno.

Little ones, how often have you been praying for Daddy? And Annie [Anneke], my curly head and little Ina [Ineke], sweetheart. I can hear you say, "Now we will have our little nap and then a cup of tea, but first count 1, 2, 3, 4, 20!" Little Janny [Jantine], sweetheart, your daddy is in God's hands, safe and well.

Bye my dear Flor, your own Menno.

～

DE GRAAF STAGGERED OUT OF THE PRIMITIVE, THATCHED A-FRAME barrack that housed several hundred prisoners. Thin and sickly,

161

he careened as he made the potentially treacherous trip to the latrine. Spotting him falter, two tall dark-haired youths in black loincloths hurried to his side. Each grabbed an elbow and steadied him as he walked onto the wobbly planks over a dugout behind a thatched wall. De Graaf was grateful. He feared that without their help, he may lose his footing, fall into the hole, and drown in the latrine like many other sick soldiers.

On his way back, he spotted the giant fig and wondered if he might find Menno there. He wobbled off the path toward the tree.

Engrossed in his note to Flor, Menno didn't notice his approach.

"Why am I not surprised to find you here?" De Graaf's smile ended in a grimace of pain. He struggled to speak. "Risking your life ... for scraps of paper that ... will never get mailed. You just can't stop, can you?"

Menno startled, but immediately recognized the voice of his best friend. He finished scratching out a few last words. "No. I can't stop hoping, Graaf." He shoved the note back into his canteen holder and looked up at his friend struggling to sit down next to him. "Graaf," he said, worried, "looks like you're getting worse!"

De Graaf ignored the comment. "Make sure you send my greetings ... to Flor and the children."

"Now you're scaring me," Menno spoke with a calm, concerned voice as he turned to face his ailing friend directly.

"There's blood in my stool. Menno, I have it now, too."

The Frisian bolted to his feet. Blood was the tell-tale sign of the dreaded, deadly dysentery. "You're coming with me!"

De Graaf grimaced as Menno helped him rise, and together they hobbled toward the makeshift medic's tent.

March 16, 1943

... Flor, life is so difficult here. So much pain, heartache, suffering and despair. I don't think it can get any worse. I, myself, feel so tired. My body is working to its limits, yet my spirit is fresh and clear.

Flor, you know, I've got a friend here who provides me with much pleasure and comfort. It is absolutely amazing. He is, it's hard to believe Flor, He is the Lord! If now I would have to do without Him and if I had to miss His Presence, that really would be the most terrifying thought!

Just a little while ago, I contacted my God about all this [suffering]. I poured out all my worries and fears before Him. Everything. I've been greatly weakened by fatigue and the starvation diet. For the first time this morning I discovered blood in my stool. Will this mean that I have the dreaded disease?

No, the only persistent thought uppermost in my mind is that I will be spared so as to one day glorify and praise His name, together with all of you. After spending time with Him this way, I feel greatly comforted and happy.

Nevertheless, I'm deeply touched and mourn often. Again, two young lives were cut short, children of God also. One died the day before yesterday. The same afternoon I had had an opportunity to talk and pray with him. Late that evening, he died. He leaves a wife and two small children. I retrieved his wedding band to be returned to his wife one day.

God's ways are not always our ways, many things are hard to understand. Yet, I'm convinced that He makes no mistakes. "Praise be to His name!" In His Presence there is only love, goodness and wisdom for His children.

My dearest Flor, oh that God would shorten this time. It is so hard for the many who suffer from dysentery or beriberi disease.

Schat, this is all for now. My sweetheart and children, I greet you all.

Love from your loving dad, Menno.

~

A JAGGED, FORKED BOLT OF LIGHTNING SPLIT THE NIGHT SKY vertically signaling the imminent arrival of a violent storm. Giant drops of rain pounded the ground while a loud, crash of thunder indicated the nearness of the strike.

Each flash momentarily illuminated the thick, dark Thai forest. Rubbery jungle palms bent as the gale intensified and became a deluge. The A-frame barrack did little to protect Menno and the two hundred others who slept side-by-side on two-foot wide wooden slabs under a thatched roof pitted with holes. As rain drove in through the open sides, a pool of slippery mud quickly formed inside.

The men stumbled from their narrow bunks to escape the rising flood water. Duffle bags, metal canteens and rubbish soon bobbed on the surface of a tributary rapidly deepening inside the barrack.

Outside, rumbling thunder followed more streaks of lightning. Drenched men faltered as they emerged from the A-frame. Many, sickly and coughing, waded through the knee-deep water, struggling to keep their balance. Suddenly an unfortunate POW lost his footing and was swept away mercilessly by the growing torrent. With water coursing around them, half a dozen dying, soaked men huddled together on an elevated patch of ground shivering, trying to keep warm.

Menno found cover under a broad-leafed tree from where he observed the pathetic scenario unfold. How it pained him to see his once proud and robust countrymen reduced to skeletal shadows cowering in misery!

March 20, 1943

Schatjes, I always eagerly anticipate the time I spend with you on paper.

God be praised! I'm doing just fine ... not a trace of the symptoms of blood and puss, that so many are suffering from.

How many reasons there are, time and time again, to be thankful to our God. And how often He receives just the opposite? There is so little spontaneous deep-felt gratitude. How much it would hurt us if our children behaved like this. We, as parents, often make mistakes and do not always act out of pure love. But God always does.

I want to thank Him today for all the special ways in which He has taken care of me. It's just tremendous. For instance, yesterday I managed to buy molasses from a couple of Indonesian boys, who were able to get out and return with lots of [cans of] them. What a special treat!

My friend Graaf is still so ill, but now I am able to bring him something every so often, like fish, bouillon, some bananas or molasses. I never imagined that these small favors would give so much joy and make the men feel so tremendously encouraged.

I guess at the time, when we had so much, we overlooked the simple things. Have we stared ourselves blind on material things, only to discover now that we have been greatly deceived?

Everything in life that is of lasting value has to start with the seed of love, joy, thankfulness, peace, etc. God is the sower. But maybe because of modern science, we thought we could skip the process and do it our way? We are discovering that the verse you reap what you sow is painfully true.

Flor, these thoughts make me glad and very thankful: to know that I'm a child of God. I realize now how easy it is to be misled. But our God promises that He will lead and guide us into all truth. Yes, even, and maybe especially, in times like these, when all else starts to fail and crumble around us. Yes, there is joy even in this dismal place!

Bye schatjes. God bless you all. Love from your dad and husband, Menno.

Deep in the jungle beyond the POW barrack, a young Thai boy crouched next to Menno behind a large fig tree. The Dutchman scanned the surroundings until he was convinced no one was watching. He loosened his Mido watch strap and gave it to the boy. The child grinned broadly and handed Menno four bananas, a floppy, gray river fish and a tin of molasses. Menno tucked the food into his backpack and nodded to the tiny boy who stared wide-eyed at the bronzed, giant Dutchman.

Eager to return to camp with his illegally traded goods, Menno moved swiftly through the forest. With the extra food well hidden, he sloshed through the muddy entrance of de Graaf's barrack.

Inside, men lay groaning on narrow bamboo planks, their ribcages protruding grotesquely. Menno found de Graaf among them. "Graaf, look what I found on the way home. Your favorite! Bananas and fish!" He tried to sound upbeat, but de Graaf was trembling. His exposed ribs, covered in thin leathery skin, rose and fell in short, shallow gasps.

"I have to go now. Have to see my wife. Is she here yet?" he asked.

"What? Your wife? What are you talking about?"

De Graaf strained to lift his shrunken, shivering frame off the bed. "Please Menno," he begged, "go see if my wife is here."

Menno realized what was happening. "Oh, dear God, Graaf, you're hallucinating!"

De Graaf grew agitated. "I must see my wife," he insisted as he struggled to get off his bed. "I must see her!"

Tears filled Menno's eyes. "My dear friend, your wife is not here. She's ... Flor ... they're all on Java."

De Graaf tried desperately to get up again. "My wife! My wife! Where is my wife?"

Japanese guards hurried to Menno's aid to help restrain the dying man. Exhausted, de Graaf succumbed. He lay back resigned to the inevitable.

Menno knelt beside de Graaf's bedside and struggled to speak, warm tears trickling down his face. "Graaf ... I must ask. If, let's say ... you don't make it back to Java ... " He paused. He never imagined he would ask his best friend this question. "Are you ready ... are you ready ... to meet God?"

De Graaf swallowed hard. He knew he was close to death. Eyes glazed and sunken, cheekbones protruding, he gradually focused on Menno's sorrowful gaze.

"Yes." Though weak, his answer was firm. "I am ready."

Menno slipped his arm under his friend's shoulder and embraced him. "Is there still something ... anything ... I can do for you?"

Graaf lifted a skeletal hand, grasped Menno's fingers and squeezed gently, his voice barely audible. "No. Nothing more to be done."

Their eyes met for a haunting moment in deep sorrow mixed with the unspoken love of brothers. As the light of life departed, de Graafs eyes lost focus. Great tears rolled down Menno's face and his chest heaved from the pain of his great loss. His best friend was gone.

DE GRAAF, WRAPPED IN A SIMPLE STRAW MAT TOO SHORT TO COVER his dirty, bony feet, made the final leg of his earthly journey the following day. Menno, the POW chaplain and two others shouldered his body to a rustic cemetery along the railroad track and placed him gently in a small, shallow plot.

Cheerful at heart, de Graaf had never been one to complain. He always chose to look at the good in life and was eager to help those around him in need. His friends honored him for his courageous attitude.

With crude shovels, they tossed dirt over his body and paused solemnly at the grave site. They turned quietly and left, but Menno lingered. Grief overwhelmed him.

Later that day Menno stole away to his forest refuge to pour out his heart to Flor. In his year of captivity, Menno had remained remarkably optimistic despite the brutality and suffering around him, but the loss of his best friend had bludgeoned him with a debilitating blow. He was at a crossroads. His hope and inner conviction became overshadowed by deep anguish of soul.

He had lost his precious wife and children, his schools and home, his beloved Indies, his position and title, his freedom, and now his best friend. His missionary calling to the Dutch Indies had cost him everything.

Menno felt alone and forsaken. Far removed from God. All seemed futile.

"Ah, ah, ah, ah!" Somewhere overhead the screeches of a jeering monkey mocked his thoughts. Emotional pain, unlike any he had ever felt, consumed his mind until his body could no longer sustain it. He covered his face with his hands and slid to the ground sobbing. For the first time on this journey he cried until no tears remained.

Time passed. His weeping subsided, but his weak frame trembled. He refocused on his notepaper and wrote:

March 25, 1943

What an awful black day it is for me! My best friend, Willem de Graaf, passed away. Right after I finished work, I went over to see him. He was laying there. All that was left of him was but a shadow. During the last days, a fever raged through his exhausted body, but he fought to stay alive to the end.

... Dear Flor, I think I know what it means when it states in the Word, "All flesh is as grass. Here today and gone tomorrow." Our colleague, John van Herp, passed away. Henk Katsma, my friend Kees Jansma and many, many others I knew. And now my best friend, Willem de Graaf.

Flor, at times, great fear overwhelms me. How small our numbers have become. What about the servants of the Lord? Has He altogether hidden His face from us and forgotten us?

"Oh Lord, again we plead with You to forgive us our debts and now, oh Lord, keep us from going down to the pit. Deliver this remnant through Your favor."

Dear Flor and dearest children, I do so hope that at least you are all healthy. My loved ones, bye from your deeply sorrowing dad and husband, Menno.

Menno's hand slid off the paper, his gaze distant. Engulfed by darkness, he was spiraling downward. He had seen it happen to many of his comrades. With the little strength left of his will, he drew from the deepest place of his fragile faith.

No! Enough! A voice deep within countered.

No matter what had happened, no matter what his situation looked like, no matter what the unknown future would hold, and — no matter if Flor and the children survived — he would set his will to trust God.

No! No! No! God will not forget us! Oh Lord, deliver us! My Flor, a thousand favors I've received here. God has NOT forgotten us!

14

NIGHT OF THE SOUL

AMBARAWA INTERNMENT CAMP, SPRING 1943

Rugged, broad-leaved Cassava bushes extended in long, straight rows under the hot Indies sun as far as the eye could see. Their starchy roots, similar to potatoes, were an important staple of the Indonesian diet, cultivated at the camp specifically to make tapioca for the internees to eat.

The female prisoners were required to work in the cassava fields to plant, harvest and dig up roots. Relentless hunger pangs gnawed at the women while they labored endlessly in the tropical morning heat. Bent over, they mechanically dug up the stubborn roots using heavy metal-tipped hoes.

For a brief moment, the Japanese guard turned his back on the small band of women, and they reacted instinctively. Flor stopped and wiped her brow, while the tall, slender woman beside her pulled off her faded blue headscarf and disappeared into the bushes. Flor knew she was scooping up snails and hiding them in her skirt pocket — a misdemeanor that guaranteed punishment if caught. The woman quickly reappeared to continue digging.

The guard turned and looked at the women intently, as though he sensed something had happened.

The woman leaned toward Flor as she dug, "A bit of protein will do you some good, Flor. You ought to try it," she whispered.

"Getting caught would not be good!"

"I'm sure your little baby Jantine would benefit."

"Jantine? She's home and back to her old self. I think her stay at the hospital saved her life."

At the guard's sudden shout, the women startled. He was announcing midday and the end of their work in fields. It was time to walk back to the camp and attend to their other duties. Work seemed endless. Aching and exhausted, the prisoners stood upright stretching their backs for relief.

With a coy smile, the slender woman winked at Flor as she patted her pocket. "Escargot on the menu tonight!"

In faded garments, soiled with dirt and sweat, the long column of Dutch women trudged back to camp, hoes resting on their shoulders.

Once through the camp entrance, they dispersed to their residences. Flor paused. Her eyes searched for Pier. Almost every day he met her at the gate, and almost every day they engaged in a similar conversation.

"You didn't call me again today, Mama," he would chide, desperately wanting to help her in the fields. He believed that would have pleased his father. "You know I want to do the heavy work for you."

The boys now lived at the completed new barrack that Flor passed each morning on her way to the fields. She couldn't make herself wake Pier even though she suspected that when he awoke each morning and found her gone, he was deeply disappointed.

Flor finally spotted Pier, but he meandered up the path unusually slowly. Together they walked back to his barrack. Flor chatted about her experiences in the field, yet Pier remained uncharacteristically subdued.

"Pier. Are you okay?" Flor asked as they sat on a bench outside his ward.

"My head," he said. "It really hurts."

Flor was alarmed. "Go lie down on your bed, Pier," she instructed. "I'll get the nurse."

Flor fetched the black-clothed nun assigned to her ward, while Pier lay on his back and covered his eyes with his wrist. His countenance portrayed fatigue. "What do you think, sister?" asked Flor.

"Don't worry, *mevrouw*," reassured the nurse after a brief examination. "Your son is merely exhausted and dehydrated. The Japs work the boys too hard. With rest he'll be back to his old self."

Dehydrated? Flor spoke a few comforting words to Pier, but as much as she wanted to believe the nurse, she struggled with an uncomfortable sense that there was something seriously wrong with Pier. He just didn't look right.

Flor left his bedside to attend to another pressing matter. All the children in the camp were required to have their hair cut to help curtail an outbreak of head lice. She sprinted off to fetch her daughters.

In the courtyard outside Flor's barrack, a hairdresser set up shop to receive the children. Flor, who had rounded up her girls, gently prodded Yelly, Hilda, Anneke and Ineke forward toward the efficient, chatty woman busy cutting the hair of a teenager. The girls, sullen and unhappy, were next in line behind two teenagers scratching their scalps incessantly.

"Mama," said Yelly, uncharacteristically sulky, "do I have to get my hair cut?"

"Yes, Yeltje, it's for your own good," Flor responded. "You'll be less itchy. You'll see."

When it came her turn, Yelly plonked herself down on the chair and whispered sweetly to the haircutter, "*Mag ik graag een klein stukje houden* [May I please keep a small piece]?"

The cocky haircutter, loud and brash, shook her head in disdain. "*Ben je helemaal gek geworden* [Have you lost your mind]?" Her strident voice carried across the courtyard. "*Het zit vol luizen* [It's full of lice]!"

With two targeted snips, the heavy braids Yelly had worn her entire life dropped to the ground, and with them, the last semblance of her thirteen-year-old sense of femininity. Tears filled her eyes as the hairdresser efficiently completed the unflattering cut. Yelly quietly yielded the stool to Ineke as Hilda looked on. Curious, the younger child climbed up eager for the new experience.

Suddenly Marjan barreled around the corner of the building, stopped, spotted Flor and headed toward her. "Flor, come quickly!" she exclaimed, breathing hard. "It's Pier. He's very sick!"

Pier's condition had rapidly deteriorated and he had been transferred to a camp medical clinic — a small, eight-bed room that treated the most seriously ill. Abandoning her daughters to Yelly's care, Flor dashed off to see him.

Frightened and breathing hard, Flor entered the room where her son lay. The doctor and nurse by his side turned to acknowledge her.

"Pier? What is wrong with Pier?" she begged in confusion.

The doctor pulled her aside and responded slowly and clinically. "We have just received the diagnosis. Pier is a very sick boy. He has *malaria tropica* — a form of brain malaria. I'm afraid, more often than not it's fatal ... " Pier moaned as fever in his body raged dangerously high.

"Fatal? No!" Flor sputtered.

Flor had not expected this! She looked at Pier once again and removed her glasses to wipe tears from her grief-filled eyes.

" ... and if malaria doesn't kill him, it could leave him with permanent brain damage," the doctor continued. "All we can do now is wait to see if his body is strong enough to fight the disease."

Seeing Flor's despair, he gently added, "When the fever breaks and Pier settles down, we'll give him a banana. If he knows what to do with it, well, that'll be a good sign."

The doctor tipped his head. "Now, if you'll pardon me, I have other patients." The over-worked physician disappeared down the hall.

For the next five days the fever raged. Each day Flor visited Pier after work dreading what she might find. Soon Pier no longer recognized her.

Early on the sixth day, Marjan, who had more knowledge about brain malaria, rose early to check on Pier's progress. She returned excited. "Flor! It's good news! Pier's fever is gone! He will get better now."

Marjan reported the news with such great confidence, Flor had no reason to doubt. As soon as she finished her work duties, she hurried to Pier's room at the clinic. It was true. He looked much better. Yet, Flor couldn't help but notice an unmistakable peculiarity about him. She touched his forehead and felt no fever, but his conversation was odd. He wasn't coherent.

"Look, Mama," Pier pointed toward the ceiling. "Isn't that a beautiful kite in the sky?"

"*Schat*, I don't see a kite," Flor responded. "You are imagining it. We are inside and there is a ceiling above us, not a sky." Pier became very angry. "That's not true!" he insisted.

Quickly he forgot the incident and moved on to another topic. "Mama," he whispered, "do you see the poor boy across from me in that bed?" Flor looked. There was no boy across from Pier. "This morning he swallowed his spoon."

Careful to avoid aggravating him again, Flor said gently, "I'm really sorry to hear that. It's good that he's better now. *Schat*, let me just go talk to the nurse for a moment. I will be right back."

Fear and alarm gripped Flor. How could Pier be delirious and hallucinating if the fever was gone? The nurse's response was evasive. She couldn't explain his behavior and appeared worried.

Pier became increasingly agitated as the day progressed. He wanted to leave, jumped out of bed and was aggressive toward the nurses. With much difficulty they restrained him and maneuvered him back to bed.

By evening he had become so violent, the medical staff could no longer manage him and concluded he must be transferred to the Ambarawa Hospital. Flor and Marjan were granted permission to accompany him out of the prison camp. Flor watched as the nurses prepared him for transport, shocked by what she saw.

Pier screamed and thrashed wildly in his efforts to resist restraint. His convulsed face was red and puffy from raging emotions and his violent kicking had shredded his pajama pants. Flor joined to help the two Indies male attendants hold him down, but the sudden sight of his mother restraining him fanned his rage. "I'm going to kill you, Mama!" he screamed, his eyes bulging with madness.

In shock, Flor recoiled.

Gradually Pier stopped thrashing. Weak and exhausted, he lay limp, lifeless, and soaked in sweat. The medical staff hurried in with leather belts to strap him to a stretcher and prepare him for the trip to the hospital.

Pier is insane! Flor thought. *Will he ever recover?* She despaired, fearing the worst.

Marjan and Flor stepped out of Pier's room waiting for the staff to begin transport. Gently, Marjan wrapped her arms around her grieving friend. Flor wept bitterly in her embrace. "What am I going to tell my husband? Our son Menno is dead!" Flor uttered between sobs. "And now, Pier! This! I don't think ... just don't think I'm going to be able to face Menno!"

Her sobs deepened into heavy groans. Marjan held her tightly and wept with her.

∾

RINTIN *POW* CAMP, NORTHERN THAILAND

March 26, 1943

How often I have begged the Lord's deliverance from this hell. It seems like it's taking forever.

Yet He has heard my plea. I still haven't come down with that dreadful disease, dysentery. But any moment, any day, this could change and then the grave is just one step away. Sometimes, freedom is so elusive and the grave so real. The food hasn't improved a bit and there is always the continuing worry about sickness and death. Now you will undoubtedly say, "Where is your God in whom you trust?"

Yes, my dear Flor, often I have so little faith and the worries seem so enormous, yet my heavenly Father appears to be so far. "Oh Lord, I plead, again and again, please save us. Yet will I praise You even under these difficult circumstances."

... [Our God] is mighty and able to deliver us. [He] is with us in this dark hour. Bye my love. Menno.

∾

THE HOOTS AND CACKLES OF AWAKENING NOCTURNAL JUNGLE FOWL intensified in the cool evening air. After a day's work on the railroad, the POWs were required to chop wood in one of the dense mountain forest clearings. Weak with hunger and sun-scorched, Menno slipped the axe from his shoulder. Together with Maliepaard, a kind, young POW, Menno hauled a large pile of wood to the edge of the clearing.

"Why are they making us do this after we've worked all day on the railroad?" the young man whispered to Menno.

"Because we're so few now. The Japs are worried the railway won't get done by year's end."

Menno suddenly flinched from a cramp in his gut. "Ouw." He stopped walking, then continued on cautiously. Suddenly another cramp pierced like a knife. "OUWWWWW!"

The stack of wood in his arms crashed to the ground and scattered at his feet. Holding his side, Menno bent over writhing in pain. Maliepaard bolted to his aid. Two decades his junior, he had a deep respect for the Frisian headmaster. Menno always seemed so strong, even indomitable, yet was kind and generous.

"Hopefully nothing's wrong?" he mused.

The next morning Menno awoke with a fever. His body trembled as he lay on the crude, wooden plank that served as a bed. Damp, misty air rolling into the POW barrack through its open sides, cast a gray hue on his skinny body.

Menno struggled as he attempted to rise from his bed. He clutched the end of the plank, but his legs buckled beneath him. Maliepaard, who shared the same living quarters, quietly appeared and steadied him. *"Heel erg bedankt, jongen* [Thanks so much, young man]."

"Do you need help … to the latrine?" Somewhat shy, Maliepaard faltered with the words in an effort to be respectful.

Menno smirked painfully. "Please. I prefer not to fall in."

The youth grinned, "You still have a sense of humor." He propped up his sick friend, and together they crept toward the barrack door.

An opaque mountain fog surrounded the POW barrack as Maliepaard gently assisted a quivering Menno toward the latrine area. Dressed in tattered shorts that hung loosely from his frame, Menno gripped the young soldier tightly as he stumbled along the muddy, dirt path. A group of tired Indies workers approached them.

"*Yameru! Kensa* [Stop! Inspection]!" The harsh command broke the morning stillness. Two patrolling Japanese guards yelled at the barefoot workers dressed in their long sarongs. The men carried coarse railroad ties on their shoulders, while a scrawny teen struggled to haul a wooden cart filled with metal spikes.

Frightened, the youth instantly released the handles, dropping the cart to the ground. He stood at attention trembling, waiting as one of the guards poked through the contents. Satisfied, the guard waved him on with his rifle.

Menno and Maliepaard re-emerged through the mist, slowly returning from the latrine.

"It's not good, is it?" Maliepaard asked sadly.

Menno shook his head. "No. Not good."

The young soldier understood. Menno had become the latest victim of the deadly dysentery that had taken so many lives. Solemnly, the two sloshed back to the barrack.

RINTIN POW CAMP, NORTHERN THAILAND

April 2, 1943

To all my greatly beloved,

What I have feared for weeks has now become a reality. I, too, have the dreaded disease, called Viral Dysentery. Of course, I would have preferred to escape this traumatic experience, but I will, like many others, have to endure it too.

It became apparent with all night stomach cramps and constant diarrhea. This morning, I noticed the danger signals — blood and slime in my stool. But don't think I'm completely discouraged. No, the Lord God will not leave me now. You, dear Flor, only you, would have understood what I've been thinking of this morning. How my heart cries out with longing for you, especially during difficult times like these.

My sweet little Phil [Hilda] is having her birthday this month and on the 29th my dear little Annie's birthday. How I would love to be home, because I am filled with remorse. While I had my dearest possessions on this earth, you and the children, I imagined other things to be more important.

What a fool, fool, fool I was! Now, I will not be satisfied here on earth until these things have been properly straightened out. Will God give me that chance or will this sickness slowly but surely rob me of my already fading strength?

~

FLOR AND MARJAN PLODDED GLUMLY BACK TO CAMP, STILL NUMB from the trauma of Pier's condition. It was a beautiful, moonlit, tropical evening wrapped in the raucous sounds of lively night creatures. Nature's charm, however, did little to dissuade Flor's profound sense of grief.

She walked, head down, distant in her thoughts. Oh, how she missed Menno! She needed him now! Who else could feel the depth of her grief? They would have found comfort in each other.

And where was God? Flor sighed. "Marjan, do you think we've all been brought here to die? Does God even care?"

Marjan walked silently for some time before she spoke. "It used to be so easy — back when life was good — easy to believe. But now … " her voice trailed off.

Flor stopped, tilted her head back and gazed at the clear, dark sky filled with innumerable galaxies and stars. Suddenly her thoughts shifted, and in an instant, she saw it.

The moon, big, bright and faithful kept shining, casting light on the little people of earth — the good and the bad — since creation. God, who created the universe to be consistent and reliable, was still faithfully there for her as much in bad times as in good. Even when her soul wrestled with pain and turmoil.

God was her maker, her partner and helper, and she needed to find His comfort. Menno could never take His place. The painful questions of her mind and soul slowly receded, making way for something new: hope! She would surrender her grief and worry, and Pier in his illness, to God. Her heavenly Father would get them through.

Then the dreaded question reappeared. If the disease took Pier's life, how would Flor be able to face Menno? No answer came, yet deep in her spirit she felt peace.

She glanced compassionately at Marjan, downcast and sorrowful. "At times like this our faith is tested." The gentleness of her voice acknowledged Marjan's pain.

"When God feels a million miles away?"

"Yes. When we wonder why God is allowing this to happen to us." Flor put an arm around Marjan's shoulders and the two resumed walking.

"What have we done to deserve this?" Marjan's eyes welled with tears.

"I don't know. I really don't. But we can't let this get the better of us." Flor's eyes took on resolve. "We can't lose our faith. If we do … then they've won, and we've lost everything!"

The two friends continued down the path. As they walked, Flor lifted her head to inhale the scent of the fresh evening air. Her stride strengthened. Somehow the chance to comfort Marjan brought clarity to the direction her own soul would take.

～

EARLY THE NEXT MORNING FLOR AND MARJAN WERE GRANTED permission to return to Ambarawa Hospital. They were unprepared for what awaited them.

The hospital staff had bound Pier to his bed with leather belts secured by screws beneath the cot. Wooden boards had been attached to its sides, yet Pier had managed to break the leather straps and kick through one of the boards. Two shots of morphine later — just one was enough to kill a boy his age — he had been reduced to an unconscious heap lying on a bed.

Flor and Marjan gaped, speechless. Pier looked dead. In silence they returned to the camp.

The next morning was difficult for Flor. She carried out her regular duties, but her thoughts were consumed with Pier. The circumstances didn't favor his recovery, yet she couldn't shake that new sensation deep within — an assurance that hadn't been there before. Fear still hovered around her thoughts, but her soul was at peace.

Barefoot, Yelly sloshed in the mud helping her mother dry the family's breakfast dishes. They picked up their belongings and headed out of the washing area when Flor heard her name.

"Mevrouw Giliam!" An impassioned, petite woman was hurrying toward them from the direction of the camp gate. "You need to go to the hospital right away!"

"What's wrong?" Flor gasped.

"I don't know. I am just delivering the doctor's message."

A rush of angst shot through Flor. *This can't be good,* she thought handing her dishes and towel to Yelly.

"Mama, is Pier dead?" Flor flinched at Yelly's morose words. How it pained her to see her faithful eldest, so hopeless. "I think Papa is dead too," she added, her eyes tormented and sad. "He's never coming back."

Flor gazed lovingly at her despondent daughter and gently stroked her cheek. "We must never lose hope, Yeltje. Please watch over the little ones while I'm gone. Especially Jantine. Make sure she finishes her breakfast. Okay?"

Yelly nodded, quiet tears rolling down her cheeks.

"Flor, let me come with you." Marjan had heard the woman's call and joined Flor's side. With a gentle nod Flor acknowledged her friend, and the two set out together, barefoot, through the camp gate and up the road to the hospital.

$\sim$

RINTIN POW CAMP, NORTHERN THAILAND

April 3, 1943

To all my loved ones,

I'm seriously ill now. High fevers are at work in my body. I took four pills made out of a plant that is able to combat these fevers. But repeatedly, I have to drag myself to the latrine all night long, only to lose blood and slime.

What made me very happy, though, was the assistance I got from a young man, named Maliepaard. He offered to hold on to me every time I had to go because the latrine really only consists of several planks placed over a narrow trench, two meters deep. A couple of men have fallen in and even died. How humiliating and deeply tragic! If you were here it surely would make all the difference in the world. But the Lord is well able to work this out also. Viral Dysentery is not known to react to any medicine. It will have to take its course. I will be patient and calmly let it happen.

Bye my dear ones. I have to rest now. Your Menno.

~

FLOR BRUSHED STRANDS OF TOUSLED HAIR FROM HER FACE AS SHE and Marjan approached the hospital room. She braced herself for the worst.

There lay Pier in his room, but not as she had expected. With a sweet, gentle expression on his young face, he slept peacefully in a normal bed. Johanna, a solicitous Malay nurse, sat by his side watching over him.

Flor was surprised and filled with wonder, until a sudden, momentary memory of Menno's peaceful face in the morgue flashed through her mind. She was confused. The nurse noticed, smiled and beckoned her to Pier's side, leaning in closer to the boy she said cheerfully, "Pier, look who's here!"

There was movement in Pier's features. Flor stared intently at him.

"Your mama's here." The nurse's melodic voice beckoned as she gently rubbed his shoulder.

His eyes opened, sleepy and heavy. He looked around until his gaze found Flor. "Mama?" he whispered.

"Pier!" Tears of relief wet her cheeks. It was wonderful to see Pier's face at peace and relaxed, and it felt so good to say his name.

Johanna was equally delighted. "Bet you're hungry, *jongen*," she said. With ceremonial aplomb, she sat him up and handed him a banana. Right away he reached for it, peeled it and ate.

"Mmm ... delicious banana!" Johanna giggled.

Pier broke into a soft smile as he chewed slowly. *Pier is going to be OK!* thought Flor. Overwhelmed with joy, she basked in a great sense of relief.

Flor and Marjan were permitted to visit Pier at Ambarawa Hospital one more time that same afternoon — another miracle.

Soon Pier was moved to a private room where he could rest. Initially his speech was slow and quiet, but his improvement was rapid. In about a week he was released to return to camp where he resumed his work in the kitchen.

Flor marveled at the speed of his recovery. God had heard her heart's cry. When she released him to God, He had intervened. Pier was healed! A miracle!

15

ON THE WAY HOME

RINTIN POW CAMP, THAILAND, APRIL 10, 1943

Inside the dimly lit medic's tent, an oil lantern cast eerie shadows across the dying men on the dirt floor. Some appeared lifeless and rigid. Others trembled with fever. Menno lay among them, thrashing and groaning in pain. *"Iemand* [Somebody] ... help! Heeeelp me!"* he cried, his voice raspy and strained. His pitiful yelps unsettled the medic.

A barefoot Malay attendant extended a flashlight over Menno's head. Deep shadows sculpted his emaciated face as he continued to writhe. He was soon joined by a tall, unshaven Dutch medic, whose stethoscope hung loosely from his neck over a blood-stained shirt.

"Heeeeelp!" Menno yelled again.

"Je voelt je echt niet goed, heh [You're not feeling well, heh]?" The gruff medic rubbed Menno's shoulder. "Let me help take the pain away."

"Het is te zwaar [It's too heavy]!" Menno cried again. *"Iemand kom me helpen* [Someone help me]!"

The medic nodded knowingly to the attendant, who handed him an injection pack.

"*Kijk eens wat ik hier heb, Menno* [Look what I have here, Menno]," he said soothingly. "*Dit zal je beter doen voelen* [This is going to make you feel better]."

The medic tapped the morphine injection pack to remove excess bubbles, while the attendant, who knew the routine well, held Menno's arm. It was time for Menno to be out of his misery. The medic quickly shot the morphine into his vein.

The attendant looked sadly at Menno's distressed face. "*Hij is op weg naar huis nu. Hij zal de morgen niet halen* [He's on his way home now. He'll be gone by the morning]."

"*Jammer* [Pity]," said the medic with resigned melancholy as he gently rubbed Menno's arm. "*Hij was een goede vent* [He was a good man]."

The men lingered a moment as Menno relaxed, became quiet and then lifeless, like the others.

"You will never experience pain again, dear friend, nor have to struggle to survive this living hell." His work done, the medic blew out the lamp's flame. Night was upon them, and it was time for all to rest.

On the other side of base camp, moonlight filtered through the open sides of Menno's former barrack, bathing the sleeping men with a few rays of weak, gray light. A rustle in the dark exposed a stealthy figure creeping toward Menno's bunk. The lanky POW found Menno's canteen and backpack hanging from a rusty nail on a support beam above his empty bed. In bold letters the backpack bore the stenciled name "Giliam."

The POW carefully lifted both the backpack and canteen from the wall and whispered to his comrade seated on the adjacent plank. "Giliam won't be needing these anymore."

"Anything good in there?" His companion tilted his chin in the direction of Menno's bag.

The men rummaged through the backpack, but extracted only a metal cup, utensils, and a tiny stub of a well-worn pencil. The taller POW rolled the pencil in his fingers and examined it in the dim light. "He sure worked this to death. Could be trouble if the Japs find it."

His accomplice snatched the pencil stub and flicked it through the open side of the barrack. With a tiny splash it submerged into a murky puddle and was gone. "You keep his bag. I'll take this." He reached for the canteen. "Could fetch a nickel or two."

THE MEDIC'S TENT LAY DARK AND STILL, INTERRUPTED ONLY BY THE occasional groan of a dying man.

The morphine was having its desired effect. Menno's eyelids were heavy, his breathing shallow, yet he felt peaceful — even joyful. Thick darkness began to envelop him. He had long decided that he was *not* going to be counted among the casualties of war, but the unthinkable was happening. Menno knew without a doubt that he was dying.

Suddenly an ethereal light split the darkness. Through it came a silhouette of a man moving toward him. Menno recognized the figure immediately.

"Are you ready to die?" asked the visitor in a firm, yet loving voice.

Menno perceived in an instant that he was not ready, and his visitor knew it. Then to his mind came the familiar words of an old Dutch hymn: *Only what has been done out of love for Jesus will last for eternity.* If his journey of suffering had shown him anything, it was just how impure his motives had been. His self-centeredness now seemed repulsive.

The man spoke again. "I am the way, and there is no other way than through me."

Menno looked around and saw that Jesus surrounded him on every side. *How wonderful it will be to tell the children at school how real the Lord is,* he thought, but suddenly realized that would not be possible. He was dead.

Menno's thoughts raced. What in fact *had* he done out of love for Jesus? What had real and lasting value? There was only one solution, one remedy to the anguish of his soul. He cried out to his Savior. *Jesus! Please! Give me another chance!*

Then, as suddenly as the vision appeared, it vanished, and Menno sank back into deep, cold darkness.

"MORNINGS COME TOO SOON," MOANED THE OVERWORKED DUTCH medic to himself as he entered the soggy medical tent. His Malay assistant had already started the morning routine of examining the rigid bodies of POWs who had passed away during the night. Crouching beside a young man, the medic gently closed his glassy, hollow eyes and nodded to the guard. As he moved on, the guard promptly removed the dead POW's body.

"Tikus, keluar dari sini [Rat, get out of here]!" yelled the Malay assistant with disgust as he kicked away a rodent gnawing on a dead man's finger.

The medic approached Menno's body. He lay still. His eyes were closed. Gently, he crouched down to study his sunken, gaunt face. "You sure gave it a good fight, ol' boy. No doubt you're in a better place ... "

Menno's eyes twitched, then opened. The medic jolted, almost toppling backward.

"Good God! You're alive!" he gasped.

Menno's lips parted and he exhaled shallow, barely audible words. "Yes. I'm … fine."

Though still extremely weak, he felt remarkably well! Peace had settled on his features. "Je … Je … sus." He attempted to speak.

"What he say?" The bewildered Malay assistant looked at his superior.

The medic shrugged. "Mumbled something like 'Jesus'? But can't say for sure."

The assistant crouched down to take a closer look at Menno and discovered his throat was parched and dry. He poured water from a canister on his waist into a tin cup, lifted his head and put the cup to his lips. Menno sipped slowly.

Amazed, yet pleased, the medic shook his head and resumed his light-hearted bedside manner. "We just can't get rid of you, can we?"

~

IN THE DAYS THAT FOLLOWED, MENNO BEGAN THE SLOW RECOVERY process. His first step: relearn how to eat. Swallowing food had become extremely difficult, and for several weeks he was only able to consume diluted tea. Eventually, he could stomach watery rice porridge followed by mouthfuls of dry, cooked rice. Soon local greens were added to his daily rations.

The meager diet, however, took its toll. Menno's skeleton-like body needed constant rest. Even the slightest movement required a great deal of effort. With eyes shut, Menno spent most of his time alone with his thoughts, lying on a hospital cot. *Jesus, I can't live if I can't eat properly,* he prayed. *I must be able to keep food down. Help me!*

One day his prayers were answered in a most unexpected way. It was the spring of 1943, four months after Menno had been cattle-carted to Rintin in northern Thailand, when Hans de Wit arrived from Singapore. A long-time friend and boarder at the Giliam home in Wonosobo, de Wit had been forced to stay behind because of an eye ailment.

De Wit approached the cadaverous body that resembled Menno with uncertainty and leaned in to study the quiet face. Sensing a presence, Menno opened his eyes. Both were startled.

"Ahhhh! Giliam?" He jumped back. "Is that you? *Man*, you look awful!"

"Nice to see you too, Wit" came Menno's swift retort with a scoff and a grin.

De Wit eyed Menno. "Look at you! Not much left on those old bones! Are you sure you're OK?"

"I'm fine. Just need to figure out how to eat again." Menno chuckled, elated to see his good friend.

He cleared his throat. "So ... you ... finally made it up from Singapore. Took the slow train?" Even in his weak condition, he couldn't resist ribbing de Wit.

This time de Wit did not compete. The profound horror of what he had already seen in Rintin had been deeply troubling. "Giliam," he said gravely, "this place is far worse than I imagined. They don't call this the 'Hell of Thailand' for nothing!"

He dug through his canvas army backpack and pulled out a few black tobacco leaves with a scrap of newspaper. Meticulously he rolled a cigarette, lit it and took a few puffs.

"Do you still have tobacco?" he asked.

"Ah ... no. I haven't smoked in ages."

He passed the cigarette to Menno. "Go on. Take a puff. It'll do you some good."

Menno propped himself on an elbow and took a few puffs. Instantly he noticed the putrid taste in his mouth disappeared.

Later his appetite returned, enabling him to eat again. The tobacco had somehow stimulated his digestive system.

De Wit inhaled and blew out smoke toward the thatched roof. "I heard Graaf didn't make it," he said wistfully. "Sure gonna miss the guy."

Menno looked down at his bunk and became introspective. "That was the worst day. The worst … " His voice trailed off. Thoughts of de Graaf's senseless death haunted him. "Thank God he was ready."

GOLDEN RAYS OF DUSK DANCED THROUGH THE LUSH, JUNGLE foliage of Rintin. Menno staggered as he inched his way along a well-trodden dirt path, clutching canes in both hands. It was time for his frail body to learn to walk again. Cringing with every step forward, he was grateful to have de Wit by his side.

"Still writing Flor?" asked his friend.

"Ya, started up again." Menno sighed.

"You stopped? Why?"

"Because all my letters got stolen the night I died," he shrugged.

"Died?"

"*Should* have died. I guess the guys thought I wasn't going to make it so they helped themselves to my belongings. Wasn't much really."

Out of breath, Menno took a break from walking and looked sadly at de Wit. "The only thing that really mattered to me were those letters."

"*Klootzakken!* [Beasts]!" exclaimed de Wit, righteously angry and offended on Menno's behalf. "Helping themselves to a dying man's possessions!"

De Wit thought a moment, then continued. "Menno, you and I both know. As soon as you're steady on your feet, the Japs will send you back to the railroad. And look at you! Your strength isn't what it used to be. You go back there ... it'll kill you!"

De Wit's words were true, and Menno knew it. "But I need a good excuse," his brow furrowed as he mused. "Something to keep me in base camp ... "

Suddenly his jaw dropped and an excitement rose in his voice. "I think I've got an idea!"

"Of course you do!" de Wit laughed. "Knowing you, you'll come up with something."

Resting on his canes, Menno nodded toward de Wit's worn-out boots. "This place could use a cobbler."

"You? A cobbler? You're a schoolteacher!"

"Ah, but I've studied the master at work." Menno's eyes twinkled with hope.

"Really? Wish I could be around to see you pull that off!"

"Heh? Why won't you?"

"I'm being sent further north," de Wit avoided eye contact as his voice dropped. "Deeper into the pit of hell. Just got word that I'll be leaving first thing in the morning."

The two friends stood in awkward silence, trying to suppress their sadness.

It had been God's pure grace that had brought de Wit back exactly when Menno needed him, and he knew it. But his heart was heavy. Yet another separation, and another person removed from his life. Would de Wit also perish on the railroad like so many others? He needed to trust God for what lay ahead.

"*Kerel* [Man], you take care of yourself. And we'll all be back in Java before you know it!"

"Yes." The grief was palpable, yet de Wit tried to remain playful. Looking up at Menno he quipped, "And this time the Heineken's on me!"

It would be the last time Menno would see his dear friend.

～

May 19, 1943

My dearest Flor and dear little ones,

I am currently a patient in an official hospital barrack not too far from Ban-Pong, and about 50 kilometers from Bangkok, the capital city of [Thailand]. I'll explain what took place since April 3rd.

That same night, I took a turn for the worse and was transferred to a small hospital in Rintin. What an enormous relief that was! At least I didn't have to grope around in the dark anymore to find the trench and make a nuisance of myself by having to hold on to my kind guide, Maliepaard.

The hospital at Rintin consisted of several tents. I had to lie on the floor, but at least I kept dry. The spot I was given had just become vacant because of the death of a POW — someone I had known well. He had been transferred to eternal glory.

On April 3rd, I still weighed in at 70 kilograms. For about a week I fought the dreadful disease, however, on April 10th the crisis finally came ...

My friends, who still visited me every day, had given up on me completely. They figured I would not see the light of day ...

But God showed His great mercy to me. I was healed miraculously!

～

MAY 20, 1943

Dear Flor,

… Slowly my strength returned to me.

One day, news arrived that our camp at Rintin was to be evacuated. The most seriously ill were to be moved to the next camp. It was not worth it to take them to the hospital in Ban-Pong, or so they figured. But those who seemed strong enough to be transported to the hospital were appointed by a Dutch doctor.

I was too weak to go to the hospital, he said, but I begged him to take me anyways. He warned me that I wouldn't survive the grueling trip by transport, but he said he would allow me to go if he wouldn't be held responsible if something were to happen to me. That is how many beriberi patients and others, including myself, found ourselves on our way to Ban-Pong.

With all the seats removed from the old truck, I tucked folded blankets under myself and tried to get as comfortable as possible. My colleague, William Lobbenzo, died during the trip. It took away the last of his strength.

~

BAN-PONG, THAILAND

June 4, 1943

Dear Flor and my little ones,

It's so strange. All I can think of is food, day and night. I've never experienced anything like it before, not even when I hardly had any food at all. I have gained at least fifteen pounds so far.

My walking is slowly getting better, although it's taking much longer than I'd anticipated. Even getting up from a reclining position takes a lot of effort. The night before last, I suddenly found myself doubled over with pain in my stomach. A possible hernia of some sort. The doctor came and gave me a morphine injection. The *next morning, I felt a lot better. Slowly but surely the pain subsided.*

But how are you all doing, Flor? How difficult it must be for you. I fervently hope that God will give you enough strength to endure and to keep putting your trust in Him ...

How He has shown His faithfulness to me. But how quickly we forget — even after He delivers us from death itself! His mercy and loving kindness endure forever.

I long for you and the little ones, Flor. Bye for now, until tomorrow.

Your Menno.

～

MENNO MARVELED AT GOD'S KINDNESS. ALL HIS NEEDS WERE continually being met. After a friend gave him some money to buy extra food, he slowly gained weight and regained his strength. But then a sudden setback.

By mid-July, he suffered bouts of kidney stones and problems with his liver. This forced him to eliminate fats from his diet, causing the beriberi disease to flare up in his legs.

Eventually, all his money ran out, and with it, access to much needed supplemental food. His weight once again on the decline, Menno knew he needed to find a solution. Maybe becoming a shoemaker wasn't such a crazy idea. But how would he convince his Japanese captors? Menno needed to find a way!

～

BAN-PONG, THAILAND

July 18, 1943

To my dearest loved ones,

I long for you all so intensely but it's taking so long ...

... Flor, I'm almost embarrassed to tell you this, but I've sold my wedding band. Honestly, I found this extremely difficult, but I thought you would prefer that I buy food instead of constantly losing weight ... maybe for at least two or three months. The ring went for 25 tikel, maybe enough to get me through to the time when we will be released! Flor, if this is what you will have to do also, go right ahead and sell your ring. Our marriage will start over again, this time with Christ in the center!

∾

AUGUST 18, 1943

Today is my dear son Pier's birthday. My best wishes for you today. I hope your birthday will be a happy one. I pray that God will multiply his blessings to you.

My dear Flor, another birthday of one of our dear children that I can't celebrate at home. How clearly I remember the circumstances surrounding our dear Pier's birth. I see myself standing there with all my shortcomings and find myself greatly indebted to you, dear Flor.

At the same time, I feel great comfort. God has chastened me severely but has not left me altogether. Yes, He has shown Himself strong on my behalf and comforted me in the greatest struggles of my life. He still is my faithful Father. Then will He also not freely offer His tender mercies for which we pray daily?

It would take another two months before the camp doctor pronounced Menno fit to return to work on the railroad. In the meantime, he had busied himself with a plan to convince the Japanese commander that he should stay at base camp to fix shoes — an extremely risky proposition. He might not have the experience or the tools, but Menno felt he had no choice. If he went back to the railroad in his current state, he would not return.

∾

BAN-PONG, THAILAND

September 25, 1943

My dear ones,

Today it's our dear little Annie's birthday. I beg your pardon. It's Ina's [Ineke's] birthday, isn't it? I wish you many returns on this day. How happy Dad will be on that day when I will be able to give you a big birthday hug and a nice present.

… My dear Flor and my dear little ones … Hardly a night passes that I don't dream about you. Sometimes I wake myself up from hollering out loud to the children in my dream and sometimes I'm preparing them a sandwich with plenty of butter and peanut butter!

My sweethearts, let's keep on hoping that one day soon, we will be reunited again. May God grant it.

~

OCTOBER 1, 1943

Mijn schatjes,

Today it's the birthday of my sweet wife, Flor. Today you are 34 years old. The Lord grant you many happy returns on this day … and we will pray that you will be my faithful, lifelong companion for many years to come. How many special reasons we will have to celebrate your birthday after God has granted us the privilege of being reunited again. May we obtain the gift of life and health from Him, especially if it turns out that we still need to be here for some time to come.

… Flor … after all this has come to an end, we will be left with a great sense of awe for our Creator. Our joy will be great, but we will owe many thanks to our faithful heavenly Father. He has supplied all of our needs. We lack nothing.

To Him be the glory and praise forever and ever. Bye my loved ones.

Your Menno.

~

OCTOBER 13, 1943

To all my darlings,

Today it's my dear little Janny's [Jantine's] birthday. My sweet little darling, a very happy birthday to you!

No doubt my little Janny won't recognize her daddy anymore and will only remember that I exist when you tell her about me or pray for me. Oh, how I wish this would be the last of the family birthdays we will celebrate separated from each other. What great joy it would be to celebrate them together again. God grant this in Your grace and mercy!

My dearest Flor ... I pray every day that God gives you strength to overcome these difficulties, and above all that you may continue to trust in Him and in His great love and power. He will make all things well. He has been so good to me.

If He has kept all of you, then soon we will have a wonderful time together. My darlings, I trust that God will grant it speedily.

Your loving Menno

PHOTOS

Dutch surrender, Java, 1942. [3]

POWs in northern Thailand, assigned to work on the Thai-Burma Railroad. [2]

Doch Hij is onze Vader: Hij zorgt
ook voor jou en voor onze kindertjes. Op deze Zondagmorg
moet ik toch zo aan je denken
en aan mijn lieve kindertjes,
dat ik je moet schrijven.
O, Fok, jij hebt de zware zorg
voor 't gezin, en dat zal niet
meevallen: ik kan mij niet voor-
stellen hoe 't gaat en waar je
eten, kleren en geld vandaan
krijgt. Doch ook dat zal in orde
komen, hoewel misschien erg
sober, doch 't is toch genoeg F

*A page of Menno's secret letters written to Florence (née Fokje)
Giliam, during captivity as a POW in northern Thailand,
1943.*

Menno Giliam's Japanese POW Registration Card.

POWs building a bridge on the Thai-Burma Railroad near Ronsi Burma, 1943.
[2]

POWs in northern Thailand, workers on the Thai-Burm Railroad. [2]

POWs in Tamarkan Camp, Thailand, 1944. [2]

Allied POW soldiers' graves in Chungkai War Cemetery, 1945. [2]

THE SHOEMAKER

THAMAKHAM POW CAMP, THAILAND, JANUARY 1944

The close of 1943 brought an end to another miserable year of war, and with it the completion of the Burma Railroad. More than one hundred thousand allied POWs and forced laborers lost their lives under the harsh working conditions, and tragically, the railway was abandoned shortly after its completion.

By early January 1944, Menno had joined the numerous prisoners relocated to Camp Thamakham, fifty-five kilometers north of Nong Pladuk, and three hundred and fifty-nine kilometers to the south of the railway's endpoint, Thanbyuzayat, Burma. The POW base, which also served as its administrative center, was immense in terms of the number of its prisoners.

According to rumors among the POWs, the tide was now turning against the Japanese in the Pacific War. Rumor also had it that the Japanese had lost many of their fighting force and were now conscripting soldiers from Korea, a country they had annexed in August 1922. The number of Korean soldiers was estimated to be as high as two hundred thousand, and they had a reputation of often being more abusive than the Japanese. When in their company, Menno moved with caution.

It had been three months since Menno's hospitalization, and his health had greatly improved. January 1944 also marked three months since his last letter to Flor. He had simply run out of note paper. It was just as well. There wasn't much spare time to write. Menno now spent long days consumed with his new job — fixing shoes.

Under the sprawling branches of a Mimosa tree, Menno set up his workshop. Sitting on a shady, sparse patch of grass, he worked with a large needle, meticulously sewing a Korean soldier's torn running shoe. Upbeat and grateful, he crooned a favorite hymn as he finished, bit off the thread and placed the shoe on an old truck accelerator pedal. Menno stood back and examined his work. Yes. It looked good — as did his future.

Thanks to all the time he had spent chatting with his friend Albert of Boazum, Friesland, Menno had observed how to repair shoes as well as make new ones. He had watched his cobbler friend resole with tar-covered thread and a curved needle; trim and harden soles with the handle of a hammer; use little wood dowels instead of nails; and work with two main tools, a last and an awl.

With some bartering, Menno managed to scrape together the tools he needed, including an accelerator pedal that became the "last" — a tool on which he fitted the shoes as he worked on them. With tools in hand, he had one final obstacle to overcome: Menno needed permission from his Japanese superiors.

Upon hearing his request, the camp commander ordered him to fix his favorite pair of shoes — a crucial test to see if Menno was trying to deceive him to avoid returning to hard labor. If Menno failed, his punishment would be severe. Aware of the risks, he worked arduously on the commander's shoes, and it paid off. He passed!

As the official camp cobbler, Menno discovered there was no lack of work. The Japanese and Korean soldiers were his first priority. If he had time, he was permitted to fix his comrade's footwear. God himself, Menno reasoned, in His omniscient fore-knowledge had spared his life by showing him how to fix shoes long before he arrived on Java.

That afternoon, Menno cautiously approached a diminutive, sun-bronzed Korean soldier. He bowed before the off-duty Korean, who sat smoking in the doorway of his barrack, and held out his repaired shoes. The soldier took them, fingered the canvas and closely eyed the stitching. After a thorough inspection, he nodded in approval. Relieved, Menno spoke, "Fifteen cents, Sir."

The Korean scowled. "You fix my friend's shoes for ten cents yesterday!"

"Yours had a much bigger hole." Menno pointed to the repaired area of his sneaker.

Annoyed, the Korean shook his head. "Too much! I give you ten cents."

"It was a lot of work!" Menno insisted. "And I broke one of my curved needles while working on it. Fifteen cents, Sir!"

The Korean, enraged, jumped to his feet. Half Menno's size, he puffed out his chest and with one swift motion slapped Menno across the face.

Menno recoiled, yet stood tall, his face inflamed and angry. "I prefer you pay me rather than beat me, Sir," he said evenly.

Incensed, the Korean lifted his hand to strike him again. Instinctively Menno threw the Korean's shoes at his feet and ran.

"You! Come back!" the soldier yelled after him.

With the Korean in pursuit, Menno sprinted full speed past the soldiers' barracks and straight to the Japanese camp commander's living quarters.

Outside the white, stucco building, a dispassionate guard with a bayonet pushed Menno back from the entrance.

"I must see the commander! Please! I must see him!" Menno insisted, flustered and panting.

"Cannot."

"Please, I beg you!" Frantic, and looking over his shoulder, Menno pleaded, "I must speak to him NOW!"

"He is bathing. Cannot."

Menno dashed off in the direction of the Dutch POW officers' headquarters. As he turned the corner of one of the barracks, he and the Korean collided.

"You, come!" The Korean, boiling with rage, commanded across the barrel of his rifle.

He had no choice. Reluctantly Menno strutted ahead of the Korean alongside the officers' headquarters, past an open window. "*Iemand haal hulp! Hij gaat me vermoorden* [Someone call for help! He's going to kill me]!" he yelled, but his efforts were in vain. Half a dozen unresponsive sun-soaked Dutch heads appeared at the window.

The guard shoved Menno into an empty barrack and forced him to kneel in submission. *Should I obey him?* he thought. *Should I let him murder me just like that?*

Pointing his gun at Menno, he rapidly scanned the surroundings, grabbed a discarded beer bottle and raised it high to smash it down on the shoemaker.

Menno bolted sideways causing the plunging bottle to miss his head. It crashed into his rib cage instead, breaking two ribs and seriously injuring another. He groaned and slouched forward.

The guard wasn't satisfied. Enraged, he picked up what was left of the bottle and with brute force brought it down again. This time the fragmented weapon slashed Menno's arm, rolled through a hole in the floor and disappeared under the barrack floor. Menno fell forward and collapsed.

Fuming, the guard latched onto his ankles and dragged him outside. *Get up! Get up!* Menno's panicked thoughts urged him. *You'll die if you stay down!*

He struggled to his feet. The Korean spotted a large stick, picked it up and beat Menno violently. Each time the bleeding cobbler fell, he jumped up as fast as he could to keep the Korean from kicking his face.

In spite of the severity of the beating, Menno rejoiced at the thought that the greatest danger had passed. Nobody gets beaten to death by a stick!

Just then a short, stern Japanese soldier ran up, pointed his gun at the assailant and placed himself in front of Menno. Stunned, the Korean stepped back. The soldier ordered both men to march ahead of him to the commander's office.

Dirt mingled with blood covered Menno's head and torso. His battered body ached from the assault, yet he stood respectfully alongside the Korean guard in front of the commander.

A Japanese translator and a hefty sergeant flanked the commander. "*Omae no uttae wa nanda* [What is your complaint]?" The commander questioned the Korean first.

Still angry, the guard bellowed, "First the shoemaker charged too much money for the repair of my shoes, and then he disobeyed me. He has shown great disrespect for the Empire. He must be punished!"

"*Kutsuya, omae no iibun wa nanda* [Shoemaker, what is your response]?" the commander probed, turning to the accused.

Although Menno's body throbbed with pain, he remained calm. "The Korean guard refused to pay me for the work I had done." Menno paused to take a breath, then continued. "His job was complicated, the tear was large, and it cost me my expensive needle. I charged him what it was worth."

The commander listened expressionless as Menno spoke. "When he started to beat me, I ran to tell you, Sir, to file a complaint, but you were bathing. Then he tried to kill me."

The commander's eyes shifted sideways as he reflected back to the events of the day. Indeed, he had been bathing, and yes, Japanese protocol required that the offended party file a complaint. The fact that Menno had rushed straight to the commander's quarters was clear evidence of his innocence. He had heard enough.

The commander turned a steely glare toward the Korean and delivered swift judgment. "Soldier, you are an embarrassment to Nippon! This man deserved his wage!" he boomed. "You had no right to try to kill him. You are sentenced to corporal punishment."

He nodded to the sergeant on his left — a muscular former Olympian who had competed in Berlin in 1936. The strapping fighter stepped forward, his fist cradled and ready.

The Korean's anger quickly dissipated into fawning, submissive fear. He had witnessed corporal punishment and knew it to be merciless. A few well-placed blows sent the guard crumbling to the floor like a rag doll, unconscious.

On his way out of the commander's office, Menno staggered to a momentary halt and shut his eyes. "Thank you, Father, you've spared my life. Again!" he whispered.

Searing pain surged through his body with every step, yet he pressed on toward the washing area. The cool water he splashed on his raw wounds stung yet brought him relief.

From the far end of the washing station, curious, bathing POWs gawked. "Looks like the Frisian took quite a beating," observed a gaunt Dutch comrade.

"I hear he nearly got himself killed for a lousy nickel," said another. The men looked incredulously at each other and carried on scrubbing their lean bodies.

MENNO'S BUSINESS THRIVED. NEW SHOES WERE UNATTAINABLE IN the confines of the large, over-populated POW base, so fixing old ones was the only option for the soldiers. With his prices reasonable, and his workmanship exceptional, the self-taught cobbler was soon unable to keep up with the demand. By April 1944 he was granted permission to recruit eight young apprentices. Menno smiled to himself: *Wait till I tell Albert. I reckon he saved my life!*

Growth, however, brought new challenges. In the shade of the Mimosa, half a dozen young cobblers, dripping with sweat, bent over a pile of threadbare shoes as they worked. Miserable, they often grumbled and complained, which irritated Menno. He had spared these young men from exhaustive and dangerous labor on the railroad. They needed to be more grateful.

In particular, Henk, a disgruntled youth, sorely tested Menno's patience. The young man suffered a medical condition that made it difficult for him to do heavy physical labor, so Menno had personally selected him. The young prisoner had been one of Menno's teacher trainees in the school system in Gombong, and he knew him well. The rigors of camp life had, however, turned Henk into a chronic complainer. On this particular morning he was in a foul mood.

"No! Not good enough," scoffed Menno as he examined Henk's work. He dismissed it with a wave of a hand and tossed the shoes at the apprentice's feet. "The stitching won't last a day! I'll give you a *tikel* [one dollar] to take the shoes back to the guard yourself if you really think they've been properly repaired." Menno knew the Koreans were particularly fussy. If the repair wasn't done well, the one who fixed it was beaten.

Muttering under his breath, Henk picked up the shoes and sat down to redo his stitching.

Menno returned to his area to resume work on a Japanese boot. He fit it onto the accelerator pedal and shook his head in disgust, thinking, *The jongen can be so sloppy!* Anger flashing in his eyes, he glanced at the youth he had reprimanded and nursed his thoughts: *I have it in mind to send him back to physical labor. Then he'll come begging to fix shoes.*

"*Koffie! Koffie! Wie wil er heerlijke warme zoete koffie* [Who wants delicious, warm, sweet coffee]?"

The voice distracted Menno from his thoughts. It belonged to one of two entrepreneurial young Indonesian POWs who came around offering the coveted treat. The other, balanced a bamboo pole on his shoulders with kettles of hot coffee dangling from each end. They had stopped among the apprentices eager to make a sale.

Menno smiled. He motioned to the youths. "Yes! Yes! Over here. I'll take enough for all of us."

Menno paid the Indonesians ten cents, and they distributed the coffee. As he sat down at his work area, he jostled the cup and spilled some of the boiling liquid onto his bare leg. "Owww! Whew, that's hot!" he exclaimed, leaping up from his seat.

"Too bad!" said a sarcastic voice behind him.

Menno spun around. "What did you say?"

"Too bad the whole thing didn't spill on you!" mocked the angry, reprimanded apprentice.

"WHAT?" Menno snapped. His temper flared. With one swift swoosh, he hurled his hot coffee at the apprentice.

"What the ... ?" In shock, the young man jumped up, his hands spread at his sides. He raised his head and looked at Menno in stunned disbelief and betrayal. His legs scalded and in pain, he bolted from the worksite.

Menno was immediately seized with remorse. Shocked at his own behavior, he ran after the young man apologizing profusely. *"Jongen.* I am so sorry! It was wrong! Please. Forgive me. I'm sorry!"

Henk was swift on his feet and quickly disappeared among the POW barracks. Having lost sight of his apprentice, Menno slowed his pace and stopped. He rested his hands on his knees to catch his breath.

With a deep sigh, he straightened abruptly. Just like in former years, his bad-tempered-self had reappeared. "Oh, God!" he cried, as deep remorse settled in. "Will I ever change?" Dispirited, he turned to head back to the worksite.

As Menno rounded the barrack's corner, before him stood a stately, tall, unfamiliar Dutch POW. Momentarily startled, he backed away and stared at the man who held a small brown package.

"Giliam?"

"Uh. Yah. That's me," Menno was puzzled. *How does he know my name?*

"Then, I believe this is yours." The man held out the package in front of him. The new POW seemed interested in Menno and studied him with a deep, kind, penetrating gaze.

Surprised and curious, Menno clutched the package, and carefully opened it. To his disbelief, there, in his soiled hands, lay all his precious notes to Flor hastily left behind in Rintin — 180 kilometers away! He never imagined he would ever see them again.

With teary eyes, Menno held the cherished papers and looked in awe at the unfamiliar figure. "How? Where ... did you ... get these?" he stuttered.

"I was told they were yours." The POW smiled, and stepped back, taking his leave with a nod.

In the shadow of the camp building, Menno was alone to savor the moment. Seated on the ground against the white stucco wall, he thumbed through the notes. Flor had suddenly and unexpectedly walked back into his life — or so it felt. *Lord, I don't deserve this!* he breathed.

Despite Menno's great personal failure, God had shown his loving kindness by returning the precious notes through someone he would never see again.

~

IN MAY 1944 AN UNWELCOME RUMOR CIRCULATED THROUGHOUT the camp: prisoners were being selected for transport to labor camps in Japan. Not long after, an official notice confirmed what Menno had dreaded. Though one of the oldest at forty, he had passed the medical examinations and had been chosen to go. Soon the reluctant Frisian would be sailing the South China Sea, traveling even further from his family.

On the day of sailing, Menno joined the queue of hundreds of young Dutch POWs being herded toward the main holding area where personal belongings were to be inspected. Tucked inside his coat was his small package of letters to Flor — his most prized possession. Menno knew they would be discovered if he didn't do something quickly. Although he appeared calm, he was far from it.

Weathered military duffel bags propped on the ground by their sides, the men assembled in groups on a muddy field anxiously waiting their turn. Japanese soldiers shoved a group of ten POWs ahead of Menno toward the inspection area. They motioned the prisoners to dump the contents of their duffle bags onto the table in front of them.

Menno felt numb as he scanned the men in the group ahead as they completed their inspection. What should he do? His turn was moments away.

Suddenly, he had an idea. Easing up to one of the men whose inspection was complete, he whispered, "Can you take this until

I'm done?" The POW didn't look his way. He scooped up the package in a swift motion and moved on.

At the table, Menno emptied his duffel bag. A chipped cup, a plate, eating utensils, a towel, worn clothes, a couple of books and his shoe repair kit. The guard pointed to his tools. "In Japan no fix shoes," he declared in a thick accent.

Menno's cherished tools had been a life-saving gift from God. He flinched as the guard carelessly sent them crashing into the bottom of a crude bin.

I guess I won't be needing them anymore, he mused, choosing to stay positive. *Maybe it's a sign the worst is behind me.*

Menno's thoughts quickly shifted to his precious notes and he dashed off to retrieve them.

THE RISING SUN

CAMP THAMAKHAM, THAILAND, MAY 1944

The first leg of the journey to Japan was a grueling two thousand kilometer transport by freight train to Singapore, equally as horrific as the initial travel by rail to Rintin two years earlier.

Again, the Dutch POWs were packed like cattle into unlit rusty rail cars. In the daytime they sweltered in suffocating heat, and at night they shivered in inadequate clothing. Food rations were meagre, and twice a day they were permitted to detrain to relieve themselves.

While the circumstances were similar, the mood and attitude of the POWs had changed. Hardened by the extreme, inhumane treatment and most vile of circumstances, they no longer feared for their well-being, nor were they anxious to leave behind what was familiar.

The four-day journey by rail delivered the prisoners to Singapore's rail station, and transport trucks ferried them to the harbor. At the dock they were forced to stand for long hours on the hot pavement under the scorching sun. By mid-afternoon, many faltered, faint from heat and fatigue in temperatures that peaked at one hundred degrees Fahrenheit.

A large French liner captured by the Japanese was designated to be their sea transport. Once Japanese civilians and soldiers had boarded, the POWs were hustled down into the hull to a poorly lit cargo hold. The little air it contained was stale, hot, and barely breathable, yet that wasn't the worst of it. The POWs quarters were infested with maggots.

Wrapped in constant semi-darkness, the men didn't know if it was day or night. They were, however, acutely aware that their Japanese transport was a moving target and would be attacked without mercy if spotted by the Allies in international waters. Trapped within the cargo hold, they would all likely perish.

Menno retrieved several books from his backpack and wrapped them in a towel for a pillow. With no bunks in the hold, he settled down on the filthy floor and was soon fast asleep.

Less than a week into the four thousand five hundred kilometer journey, chickenpox broke out among the passengers. Older POWs like Menno suffered the most. Twice he was taken on deck for guards to douse him with cool, salty water.

On this day, he leaned his head back and caught his breath as the refreshing seawater sloshed over him. Though the water initially stung, it brought immense relief from the itchy red welts covering his body.

Dripping from head to toe, Menno wandered toward the rusty metal railing to dry himself. The sight of the spectacular, endless blue sea revived his soul. He drank in the view, but inadvertently spotted two Japanese destroyers flanking the ship with low-flying reconnaissance aircraft hovering overhead. Eager to share his insights with his comrades, he suddenly remembered that observation of Japanese military activity was strictly forbidden.

But it was too late. A guard had noticed.

"Kotcha Koi [Come here]!" A menacing Japanese voice spoke the dreaded command that implied a punishment was imminent.

Gripped by fear, Menno bolted to the stairway, but realized that was a mistake. How was he to escape in a ship's hold? The punishment would be worse when the guard found him. He stopped, turned and walked back submissively.

In a few steps the soldier was beside him with his gun raised like a baseball bat. Blow after blow landed on Menno's head splitting his eardrum. Excruciating pain exploded in his ear. Menno fell to his knees, holding his bleeding head. As he staggered to his feet, the guard relented and much to his relief, released him to go back to the hold. *Best not share the news of the military maneuvers with the others!*

The following night the ship was approaching a Japanese harbor when its warning siren sounded. American aircraft roared overhead and swooped low, dropping bombs mere yards away. The ship lurched and tilted from the force. Japanese destroyers exchanged fire with the American fighters but missed, and the planes sped out of sight into the night sky.

The exchange of fire had woken the prisoners, but Menno only learned about it the next morning. He hadn't heard a thing. With his damaged ear completely deaf, he slept soundly on his good ear throughout the ordeal.

~

ON JUNE 6, 1944, THE DIFFICULT TWO-WEEK JOURNEY BY SEA brought Menno and his POW compatriots to Modji, a port city on Kyushu Island. Rumors circulated that Allied Forces had crossed the English Channel to attack the Germans that day. If true, did it signal the end of the war was near? The Japanese scoffed at such an absurd notion.

Last to disembark, the prisoners emerged from the hold squinting and covering their sensitive eyes. The sudden exposure to daylight and the sights of the unimaginable new world before them were overwhelming. Modji was a busy hub of cars, horns, traffic, animals and tiny dark-haired Japanese moving about freely. They gawked at the people engaged in normal daily activities, the smells of food from vending carts, and most especially the towering buildings, the likes of which they had never seen.

Distracted drivers and passengers stopped to stare at the filthy, unshaven, bony giants herded by armed Japanese soldiers through the city's busy market square. Through office windows carved into the colossal buildings, young female workers stared transfixed at the peculiar parade below.

The POWs slowed their pace as they took in the foreign surroundings. Jan, a POW next to Menno, tipped his chin upward. "Never imagined buildings *this* tall!"

"I reckon they never imagined people *this* tall!" Menno pointed to his comrades, and to the group of curious local pedestrians stopping to ogle the Dutchmen twice their size. An anxious Japanese mother drew her wide-eyed two-year-old boy closer, away from the foreign giants.

Menno caught the threatening glare of a guard directed at him and shuddered. *What would it be like to be at that man's mercy?* Just then the guard yelled at the POWs to pick up their pace and keep marching. Menno leaned over to Jan, "Too much of a show for the locals. I guess it's making him nervous." Hungry, fatigued and numbed by their new environment, the men pushed forward.

THE POWs WERE COMPLETELY UNPREPARED FOR WHAT AWAITED them next. They journeyed again by rail, but this time on passenger trains with proper seats and windows. They felt like royalty! What a joy to watch the passing countryside as the train snaked its way to Nakama, fifty kilometers north of Fukuoka, and one hundred and ninety kilometers north of Nagasaki.

Upon their arrival at Nakama Branch Camp, Fukuoka 21, the men were assigned to tidy, clean barracks with a beautiful dining room and adjoining kitchen. They settled into their bunkhouses before being called to dinner — a hearty, delicious bowl of vegetable soup.

In Japan, life began to take on a semblance of civility, and for Menno, it also offered somewhat of a reprieve. Rather than being assigned to difficult work in the coal mines, he was relieved to hear he had been appointed to kitchen duty along with two other prisoners, Jacob and Levi. As kitchen helper to Jacob the cook, and Levi the head of the POW kitchen, Menno was expected to perform numerous menial tasks. But it meant never having to set foot in the mines, for which he was particularly grateful.

Menno also thanked God that he did not have to deal directly with the harsh Japanese captain, the overseer of the mining camp. Instead, he and his fellow prisoners reported to the captain's subordinate, a brigadier, and to his son Matsumo, a soldier. Menno and Matsumo developed a friendship and conversed often. As their mutual trust grew, Matsumo shared his future dreams with him.

At the request of the young Japanese soldier, Menno agreed to secretly teach him English from the only English language book he had, his Red Cross Geneva Convention Bible. The opportunity to instruct and encourage someone brought Menno a deep sense of satisfaction, as did sharing stories about God. Their friendship continued to flourish.

In exchange, Matsumo agreed to hide Menno's notes to Flor during inspections. Though it was forbidden, it was a risk they were both willing to take.

18

BE "FLINK"

AMBARAWA INTERNMENT CAMP, CENTRAL JAVA, SEPTEMBER 1944

Tattered clothing dangled loosely from the bodies of the barefoot women and children bowing before the Japanese camp commander. Hands behind his back, he sauntered among the rows in his immaculate, pressed uniform and shining leather boots. With a dark scowl, the commander reveled in his power over the defenseless prisoners forced to stand bent over for long stretches of time. Each internee knew the drill well. One after the other they shouted their designated number.

Hilda leaned toward her mother and whispered, *"Mama, ik heb zo'n ontzettende dorst* [I'm so very thirsty]!"

"Shhhhhh!" Flor's eyes shot back, beckoning Hilda to be quiet. One must not be caught speaking during roll call.

"Kyu-ju san [Ninety-three]!" yelled a prisoner in Japanese from the back row.

"Kyu-ju yon [Ninety-four]," followed the woman next to her.

"Kyu-ju go [Ninety-five]."

The counting stopped, filling the air with tension. They dared not glance back to see who was missing. The awkward silence was broken only by a baby's faint whimper. One of the guards duly noted the absentee and resumed in an icy tone, *"Tsuzukero* [Continue]!"

"Kyu-ju nana [Ninety-seven]! A teenaged girl.

"Kyu-ju hachi [Ninety-eight]," said the last prisoner.

The counting was done. Women, sweltering in the heat, groaned from exhaustion and pain.

"Naorei [Stand erect]!" the commander ordered.

Many of the older women struggled to steady themselves as they tried to stand upright. Suddenly, a sick, elderly woman collapsed behind Flor. She swung around to see a soldier appear and kick her with his leather boot. Battered and injured, the woman sank into unconsciousness in a pool of blood. A wave of nausea passed over Flor.

The camp translator, a severe British woman with bobbed, graying hair and glasses, stepped forward and with authoritative aloofness shouted, "Boys twelve years and older will be transported to an all-male camp."

The women gasped and looked from one to another shocked by the unexpected announcement.

"Ensure bags are packed and ready for transport at 0800 hours tomorrow morning." Emotionless, she nodded to the camp commander and took a step back.

"Sagarei [Dismissed]!" yelled the commander.

Quiet sobbing broke out in various parts of the field as clusters of women gathered to console each other. Grief stricken, some quietly slunk away with heads bowed.

Flor stood motionless. Soon Mieke and Marjan came to embrace her. They were weepy, but Flor was livid. "I am not going to let him go!" she insisted. "He's only twelve years old!"

"Oh Flor! After all you've been through!" Mieke moaned.

"Why?" cried Marjan, shaking her head at the senseless cruelty. "I don't understand! What's the point?"

Flor felt a tug at her arm. "Mama, do I have to go?" She turned to see the anxious eyes of her affectionate son, now almost her own height. "*Schat*, I don't want you to go!" She pulled Pier close and wrapped her arms around him. Her eyes welled up with tears.

There was no getting out of it, and she knew it.

Later that day the women prepared their boys for departure. They feared the worst. Would their sons be transported to an undisclosed destination in a far corner of the Indies island? To everyone's relief, they learned their sons would only be located to an all-male camp in another part of town. Despite its closeness, the women would not be allowed to make contact with them.

~

UNDER A RUMBLING, OVERCAST SKY, FLOR AND PIER CHERISHED their final moments together as they trudged through an abandoned tennis court, cracked and overgrown with weeds. It was still early, but the air was thick with humidity. Sweat began to form on their bodies.

Pier carried what was left of his few belongings in one of the family's well-worn suitcases. He wore baggy, discolored shorts — his only pair. A stray red marble, overshot by children playing a game of *knikkeren* nearby, rolled to his feet. Pier instinctively kicked it back. Absorbed in the game, the children giggled as they resumed their play.

Wisps of Flor's short-cropped hair framed her maturing face. Faded and stained, her tired floral dress caught a gentle breeze as she walked barefoot. There was so much she needed to tell Pier, yet not enough time. Where would she begin?

"Promise me you'll say your prayers every day ... " she urged, her voice serious, but loving.

Pier didn't look up. He nodded.

"And whenever you have problems and don't know what to do ... "

"Yah, Mama. I know."

"And you'll always conduct yourself in a way that is honoring to God."

"Yah, Mama."

Flor stopped and turned to face Pier who looked expectantly at her. She placed her hands on his shoulders and gazed into his eyes. Her beloved Pier! His childhood had come to an abrupt end. What was he about to face?

It was so important to Flor that Pier knew he would not be alone. There was One who would always be by his side; One who would guide him; warn him; protect him. If only she could impart into his soul what had taken her a lifetime to learn! She chose her words carefully.

"Even if ... things get very difficult, you're never to steal. Or to lie. It could do you more harm than good. Do you understand?"

He absorbed her words and nodded.

With an aching heart, Flor lovingly stroked his blond head. "I will pray for you every day, *schat*. I know the Lord will be with you." Pier nodded, crestfallen. "But I'm supposed to help you!" Choking back tears, he hugged her.

Flor put an arm around him. They resumed walking. Dozens of weepy mothers and despondent, barely clad boys had gathered by a fruit lorry where two stern soldiers stood guard. Some boys, glum and resigned, already in the truck's open back, leaned on the rail. One mother sagged into her friend's arms and wailed.

The approaching rain cloud brought a sudden tropical deluge. Flor's wet clothes clung to her meagre physique exposing her bony hips. She looked at her son. The rain ran down her face and past sad eyes filled with love.

Just then the impatient lorry driver leaned out his window and honked several times, warning of the truck's imminent departure.

"Pier, *je moet now een flinke jongen zijn hoor* [you must now be strong]," Flor said as much to herself as to him. Then her countenance lightened. A sparkle lit her eyes, and she smiled. "You know what? I think you're going on an adventure!"

A smirk curled the corners of Pier's lips, and a look of mischief appeared in his eyes. He gave his mother a tender kiss on the cheek, stepped up to the lorry, tossed in his dripping case and bounced into the back. He moved in along the rail among the other blond boys and waved to Flor. As the vehicle lurched forward, they grabbed each other to keep from toppling.

Thunder rolled, and rain pelted the small, weepy crowd waving to their beloved sons. Soaked, Pier moved to the back and yelled, *"Flink zijn* [Be strong]!"

Will I ever see Pier again? Flor stretched out a hand and waved one last time, her heart reaching out to him as the transport disappeared from view.

~

IN JANUARY 1945, FOUR MONTHS AFTER THE BOYS HAD BEEN relocated, the internees were faced with another unexpected announcement: Ambarawa would be turned into an all-male camp. Resident women and children were given mere days to prepare for evacuation. Flor rushed to pack the children's back-packs to take as much as possible with them.

Half the women and children were immediately sent to the internment camp in Moentilan, Java, while Flor and her girls were moved to Ambarawa Ward 9. Boys, ten years and older, were to stay in the men's camp — another heart-wrenching hurdle for many mothers like Mieke, whose son Bram was to remain. Several transports of sickly, older men arrived to fill the vacated spaces.

To make matters worse, the night prior to their train departure was filled with terror.

An intense gun battle broke out between the Japanese and their Korean subordinates, the latter having been accused of mutiny. The loud fighting seemed very close, even in the same building, and continued throughout the night. Frightened women and children cowered on the floor, as mothers shielded their youngest. "They're going to shoot us," wailed Hilda. Flor, not convinced of her own words, forced herself to say softly, "*Schat*, they are fighting amongst themselves. We are safe here." Fearing for their lives, no one was able to sleep.

With the arrival of dawn, the shooting finally subsided. The internees were promptly told to gather their belongings and ready themselves for the trip ahead — on empty stomachs.

Exhausted and hungry, the women and children set out barefoot to the train station amidst the chaotic yelling of the Japanese guards. Even if they had eaten, it would have done little to miti-gate the chronic, gnawing hunger pangs they constantly experi-enced. Lethargic, they stumbled ahead, burdened by their heavy backpacks. Above the jostling crowd, Yelly's head bobbed as she willingly ferried Jantine on her back. Flor kept the rest of her daughters close by her side.

They waited all day at the station. As evening approached, Japanese soldiers arrived with an array of local delicacies and spread them on tables along the platform. The women and children were elated, anticipating the food was for them. Their hopes were soon shattered. The Japanese officers gorged themselves, while the prisoners looked on. Guards with loaded rifles stood between them and the feasting officers.

At sunset the women and children were permitted to board the train — the same one that had brought the sickly men to Ambarawa. Under the scrutiny of the Japanese soldiers, Flor and her children climbed aboard and made their way to crude wooden benches. The stench and filth shocked them. Flor clutched her stomach to fight nausea.

"Look, Mama! Poop!" Hilda exclaimed pointing to human waste on the floor.

"It's everywhere!" said Anneke, looking up and down the car with disgust.

Flor didn't stop to assess the situation. Her hair a mess, and her dress sticking to her sweaty body, she continued to push the children along.

"Het stinkt hier zo verschrikkelijk [It stinks here terribly]!" complained Inge, while following closely behind her mother.

Mieke's face contorted at the stench. "What have we become? Animals?"

The children hesitantly found a bench to sit on. Flor, Yelly and Mieke lay their meagre belongings on the wooden shelves overhead. With Jantine cradled on her lap, Yelly gazed morosely out the locked glass window.

Hilda stood by Flor's elbow. "We haven't eaten all day!" she moaned. Ineke plonked herself on her mother's lap and began to sob. *"Mama, ik heb ontzettende honger* [Mommy, I am so hungry]!"

Flor could see fear and anguish in her children's eyes. No matter how she tried to shield them, Japanese occupation was a grueling ordeal. Flor despaired for her little ones.

"Lieve schatjes, food will come," she said, calmly stroking Ineke's fine, light brown hair. "We must be patient. It's late, and we're all so tired. Let's try to get some sleep, heh?"

The children glanced around obediently to see how they might lie down on the narrow benches. Mieke and Inge looked at the putrid floor and reluctantly decided to settle down on it for the night. Yelly and Flor were revolted. "I am not going to sleep on poop!" said the fifteen-year-old under her breath.

The younger children eventually drifted off to sleep on the floor, but Flor and her eldest just couldn't get comfortable on the narrow benches. They were both still wide awake at midnight. Suddenly Yelly straightened, leaned close to the window and became animated. "Mama!" She said in a loud whisper. "Mama look!" With great excitement she pointed out the window. "Look! It's Pier!"

"Pier?" Flor jumped to her feet leaning over Yelly to see where she was pointing. "Are you sure? Where?"

"There, Mama, see?" Yelly pointed to a group of scruffy Dutch boys carrying mattresses onto the platform.

There he was, still wearing the same oversized khaki shorts. He looked tired, pale and thinner. "Oh no!" Flor's heart ached for the boys. "The nights are getting cold and all they have on are those flimsy boxer shorts."

She banged on the window. "Pier! Pier! *Kijk hier* [Look here]! Pier!" Hilda, Ineke and Anneke were awakened by their mother's shouts. They quickly gathered at the window hoping to catch a glimpse of their brother.

Mieke and Inge joined in to try to get Pier's attention. But all attempts failed. Pier was oblivious. The darkness of the night, with the added commotion on the platform, drowned out their efforts to reach him. Just meters away, he had missed a rare opportunity to see his family.

They continued to look on as the boys finished stacking the flea-infested mattresses that belonged to the women and children about to be transported. A guard outside barked orders, and the boys turned and marched out of view.

Heartbroken, Flor slumped onto the wooden seat, her eyes moist with tears. She sat lost in thought, staring at the platform where Pier had stood.

Yelly, too, was quiet. Tacitly, she returned to the hard, narrow bench next to her mother, to attempt, again, to fall asleep. A while later, exasperated, she bolted upright and uttered in a loud, frustrated whisper, "Mama, I can't sleep! I'm going to lie down on the disgusting floor."

There was no alternative, and Flor knew it. She had been resisting the thought herself. "Please, *schat,*" Flor tried to comfort her, "try to get some rest. I will join you." Yelly grimaced yet conceded. She slid awkwardly onto the floor. Flor sat for a few more minutes before slowly lowering herself next to Yelly.

As light dawned, Flor woke and found the train hadn't moved. Some of the women and children were pressed against the windows at the sight of a load of freshly baked bread arriving on the platform. They cried out hoping the food was for them. Again, it was not to be. In tears they watched as it was distributed among the guards.

Finally, late that Sunday morning the train lurched forward. From her handbag, Flor pulled her worn pocket Bible wrapped in a crocheted handkerchief. She moved the tiny book near the glass to catch the light, when she recognized familiar landmarks. There, on the hill, outside Camp Ambarawa was the tiny cemetery. *Menno's gravesite!* Its frail wooden cross was almost completely overgrown with grassy weeds.

The train's wheels screeched as it careened around a bend sending a chug of black fumes toward the hill. Flor's gaze lingered on the cemetery until it was out of view. She continued to stare out the window, her thoughts focused on her lovely little Menno and her eyes moistened. How she missed his tender, kind spirit. With her Bible clutched close to her chest, Flor settled back onto the bench as the train jostled and squealed forward. Closing her eyes, she sobbed.

THE TRAIN JOURNEY FINALLY BEHIND THEM, THE FORMER AMBARAWA prisoners trekked one and a half hours by foot to their new home — Solo internment camp in central Java. Encrusted with excrement, they stumbled barefoot along the rough country road, under the scorching sun. Two days without food brought many to the point of complete exhaustion. Yet, some women still attempted to carry their little ones. Flor stopped momentarily to reposition Jantine in the cotton sling on Yelly's back. The other girls, weary from dragging their suitcases, paused to rest. Mieke lagged behind, sweating profusely under her husband's heavy military helmet.

"Mama, I am really thirsty," pleaded Hilda, clutching Flor's skirt.

'I know, *lieve schat*," her mother assured her. "There'll be water. When we get there."

"Do you know for sure?" She persisted.

"Yes, *lieve schat*."

"Will there be enough for everyone?"

Flor grabbed Hilda's hand and bent over to look into her child's desperate eyes. She kissed her sweaty forehead. "Yes, enough for everyone," she consoled her gently.

Suddenly, a tiny elderly woman collapsed on the road. *"Anata o taidana josei ni shiyou* [Get up, you lazy woman]!" yelled the young Japanese guard, who appeared moments later.

With all her strength she tried, but failed, collapsing into a heap. The guard kicked and beat her, but to no avail. Robotically, other prisoners trudged by without stopping.

Eventually, two Japanese soldiers arrived with a horse-drawn cart carrying half a dozen collapsed women. Like a sack of sand, they tossed the elderly woman onto the wagon. She landed on top of another limp body already expired from over-exhaustion.

Upon arrival at Camp Solo, the prisoners felt a tremendous sense of relief. At first glance, the main camp building actually looked pleasant and livable, but that impression was short-lived. They were moved into a crude bamboo barrack with a dirt floor and bamboo tables for beds.

The children, weak with fatigue, were barely able to stand. Flor immediately set about making beds and stacking luggage underneath the tables, while Yelly took the young ones to the washing area. Once the room was prepared, Flor left to join them.

"You're new here," a voice said behind her. She turned to see a Dutch woman in a faded paisley dress.

"Yah. We just arrived from Ambarawa."

"They told us you were coming," the woman looked upset. "They said the group from Ambarawa was to be punished for some crimes and won't be given any food."

Flor paled. "Crimes? What crimes? No food?" Her knees buckled. She felt faint.

"And now *we* can't eat either, because they shut down all the ovens," added the woman.

Flor stumbled back inside the empty barrack and followed the wall to the nearest corner. Crushed and defeated, she slid to the floor and held her knees close to her chest. That was the final blow. She simply had no strength left. Wretched sobs burst from her soul, and tears flowed. Flor heaved as she wept uncontrollably.

Soon she felt a gentle arm wrap around her. Someone had seated themselves by her side. Flor's upward glance was met with the kind, compassionate eyes of chaplain *Mevrouw* Slotenmaker-de Bruyne. "Dear," said the cleric with great empathy, "I will get you something to eat."

Moments later she returned with a small amount of food that included a bit of brown sugar. The sweet taste brought comfort. Soon Flor started to feel better.

"I just don't know, *mevrouw*," whispered Flor, "if I can keep doing this. I just don't know ... "

"When we are weak, then He is strong." The familiar Scripture spoken gently by the chaplain brought peace to Flor. She shut her eyes, took a deep breath, and with the help of *Mevrouw* Slotenmaker-de Bruyne rose slowly to her feet.

With a heavy heart and halting steps, Flor made her way back to the bunks and together with the chaplain hung mosquito nets around the beds — necessary protection from malaria-bearing mosquitoes.

Soon the children returned, barely uttering a word. With great effort they strained to climb into bed.

The years Flor and the children spent in Ambarawa were filled with great suffering, yet Camp Solo proved to be far worse. Unparalleled fear, uncertainty and death became their constant companions. Many gave up their will to live.

As conditions deteriorated, Flor observed a widening distinction between those who did not believe in God, and those who had a living faith. Whenever a loved one, especially a child, died, heartbreak and grief followed. Those with faith believed with all their hearts they would be reunited with their loved ones, and it gave them hope. They shone in times of despair and were envied by the others. Based on their living faith in God, their confidence offered genuine comfort and peace to the others.

Those who had committed themselves to a lifetime of service to God, like missionary Margaretha (Margot) Adriana Alt, unselfishly helped the women who had fallen into despondency. She held regular Bible studies in small groups and wrote songs that introduced many to the Scriptures. Convinced that only Jesus could bring mankind into a genuine relationship with God, Margot talked about Him with sincere and heartfelt conviction.

19

PRISONERS OF HOPE

Nakama, Japan, Spring 1945

Golden rays of sunlight danced across the neatly organized supply shelves of the kitchen storage room attached to the POW barrack. An amber evening hue surrounded Menno and Matsumo sitting side by side at a table at the back of the room. Both appeared slightly on edge.

Uncharacteristically tall, the young Japanese soldier wore a crisp, fitted uniform. Through round, metal-rimmed glasses that clung gently to his sculpted face, his studious eyes scrutinized Menno's worn, black Bible resting on the table in front of them. Menno leaned toward Matsumo and spoke in a hushed tone, "Did you bring something to write on?"

Matsumo produced a few sheets of crude paper from his bag and dropped a series of colored pencils on the table. "Okay. Good. That'll do," Menno responded as he flipped through the Bible. There it was — the passage he was looking for.

"Today we'll read the story of Joseph." Pointing to the text, he read each word slowly and carefully, "Joseph, a young man of seventeen was tending the flocks ... "

He glanced at Matsumo. *Odd,* he thought. The soldier did not attempt to write a single word, nor did he ask questions. Instead, he listened carefully.

Eventually Matsumo picked up his colored pencils and began to draw. Menno continued to read. Soon a detailed image of a warrior in a multi-colored robe came to life. Menno paused. In all his years of teaching, he had never met a student like the young soldier. Delighted with Matsumo's ingenuity, Menno pointed to Joseph's aggressive Japanese features and joked, "Joseph — a Samurai warrior! Ha!"

Matsumo stared earnestly at Menno, taking each word seriously.

Suddenly a loud bang! The door to the storage room flung open startling both men. Menno hid his Bible, while Matsumo shoved his drawing into a bag.

Jacob, the short, dark-haired cook, stood in the doorway bewildered to find Menno with a Japanese soldier. Without a word, or a glance, Matsumo picked up his bag and with a few strides walked past the cook and out of the storeroom.

Jacob watched the Japanese soldier leave, then turned to Menno. "Giliam, are you crazy? You know his father is the brigadier who runs this place. Japs can't be trusted!"

Menno stood to leave. He felt defensive and defiant. "Matsumo is different," he retorted.

"Different? What exactly are you doing with this boy?"

He slowly pulled out his worn pocket Bible. "I'm teaching him English. Using … this."

"Great!" the cook mocked, turning to lift a large bowl from a shelf. "The officer will be very pleased when he hears his boy speaking Bible English with a Dutch accent!"

Menno tucked the precious book into his backpack. "Matsumo is a trusted friend. He's been willing to hide my letters during inspections. I'm returning a favor."

The cook was amazed. "You trust him with letters to your wife? Giliam! He's the enemy!"

Both Menno and the cook turned toward the door. "Yes, but even the enemy has a soul. Jacob, if I can help this one boy — show him some kindness — maybe he'll see there's another way besides fighting and war."

The Dutch cook wasn't convinced. "You'll never catch me doing anything nice for a Jap. After what they've done to us, they don't deserve it."

"Nor do I," Menno's eyes were soft and earnest. He understood Jacob's response. "Yet God gave me a second chance."

Menno's love for the Japanese soldier seemed genuine, and it baffled the cook. He shook his head as the two men slipped out of the storage room, Menno quietly locking the door behind them.

LIVING CONDITIONS FOR THE POWs HAD IMPROVED CONSIDERABLY, yet they were still plagued by constant hunger. Forced to exist on an inadequate diet, they became obsessed with food. The mine workers, in particular, received barely enough to sustain them through the long days of heavy labor. This made the job of the kitchen staff challenging at times. Their every move was scrutinized by both the Japanese and the other prisoners. All were leery that the ones working with the food would sneak extra for themselves. Every bowl of rice was checked, and on occasion, the kitchen workers were required to dump their food back into the pot and have it remeasured.

In the winter of early 1945, food had become increasingly scarce, and hunger among the Dutch prisoners was insufferable. One day Matsuma informed Menno that the POW kitchen was about to receive a special treat — shark meat. The prisoners waited with mouth-watering expectation, but a last-minute decision diverted the meat to the Japanese kitchen. Menno was indignant. *That is completely unacceptable,* he thought as he stormed off in the direction of the brigadier's office.

With appropriate humility, Menno approached his superior. "Sir, with all due respect, it is the POW kitchen's turn to have the shipment of shark meat. The Japanese kitchen just had their turn."

The brigadier stepped back in shock at such a bold gesture — one he had never encountered from his subordinates, let alone from a POW.

"Who do you think you are to tell me what to do?" came the swift retort. "Do I have to remind you that you have no rights here? You are a prisoner of war and you are my enemy!"

Bursting with anger, the brigadier screamed, "Return to your duties. Now!"

Undaunted, the headstrong Frisian stood his ground. "Sir, I have learned that you are a good and fair man who does the right thing. If I may say so, I ceased to be your enemy the moment I became your prisoner of war. In fact, sir, I have considered you my friend, and I believe you consider me to be your friend."

Menno had made a valid point, and the military leader knew it. On many occasions he had willingly helped the brigadier recover from a drunken state. He had routinely escorted his superior to a small, airless basement room where he slept off his stupor. Since remaining in the enclosed space for more than an hour could have been fatal, Menno always made sure to wake him at the right time. "Would an enemy have done that, sir?" Menno asked gently. "As a friend I am pointing out that it is our turn to be served some meat."

Without another word the brigadier invited Matsumo and a secondary officer into his office. After a brief discussion he returned. "Okay, Giliam. The meat will go to you this time."

With a sigh, Menno thanked God for the blessing.

On another occasion, he benefited from the prisoners' barter economy. A mine worker approached him. "The other day I saw you hang out a rather large piece of canvas. Where did you get it?"

"It was a gift from my wife when she visited me in Djatibarang, on Java. I was stationed there to blow up the railway to stop the Japs." Menno had been hauling the material with him since his capture three years earlier. "My wife thought I could use it as a bed."

"Oh, I see," the man sounded disappointed. "It has a lot of meaning for you. I was going to ask if you might want to sell it, but ... " he shrugged.

"Well," Menno replied quickly. He had already been thinking of selling it for money to buy extra food. "For the right price, I might consider."

"I don't have any money," the worker said, "but I could trade you for some rice."

Menno thought a moment. "I could do that."

"How many bowls of rice do you want for it?"

"Fifteen."

"No. That's too much." He paused for a moment as he contemplated a counter-offer. "How about thirty?"

He misheard! Menno realized. "Alright, then. Thirty will do," Menno shrugged and grabbed the offer. The prisoner had understood fifty rather than fifteen. What providence!

For thirty days Menno rejoiced as he enjoyed an extra bowl of rice that he ate secretly in the kitchen to avoid jealousy. With hunger a constant companion, an extra bowl was a feast!

At times Menno was asked to travel with one of the Japanese officers into town to stock up on food supplies. On one occasion he accompanied a sergeant who was advanced in years — a veteran of the Manchurian war. An interesting and kind soul, the older man invited Menno to his home to meet his family. This proved to be the highlight of Menno's time in captivity. To his great surprise, he was invited by the sergeant's wife to stay and enjoy a delicious Japanese meal.

Menno attributed these unexpected blessings to God's goodness and he was always quick to give thanks. But how long would the favor last? His Japanese captors seemed increasingly desperate as the war dragged on.

∿

"NAOREI [STAND ERECT]!" THE COMMANDER ORDERED.

On the muddy field hundreds of drenched, bent over women straightened mechanically. Their lifeless faces grimaced in despair. A tropical downpour continued to pound the ground around them. No one dared to flinch. The commander, his translator and the European camp proctor, all protected by large black umbrellas, eyed the prisoners closely.

Some women stood in undergarments — the only clothing they had left. Downcast children lined up behind their mothers. Thunder rumbled in the distance.

Above the sound of the pounding rain the translator yelled instructions.

"If your name is called, come forward immediately." She nodded toward the proctor who held a box of white postcards bearing red stamps. "You will receive information about your husband."

A soft murmur, and gentle stirring occurred among the women. Maybe good news was on the way?

"Once you've received your card, you are dismissed," she hollered above the elements. "Corrie Baas, Nelly Bakker, Rita Bos, Tineke Berg, Marian Berg, Hilda de Boer — hurry ladies. We don't have all day!"

As names were called, women stepped forward to collect their cards. Almost immediately great shrieks of grief erupted. Some women collapsed on the muddy ground. Others howled. Most walked slowly to their living quarters, quietly clutching the final, torturous word of their beloved's fate stamped in blood red on the white *DECEASED* card.

The translator continued: "Hetty Westhuizen, Anna Wit and lastly Mien Zijlstra. The rest of you are dismissed."

Flor's wet hair pressed against her forehead. She stood in the pouring rain, shaking, eyes closed and breathing deeply. She was one of the fortunate ones whose name had not been called. *Does this mean Menno is still alive?* she wondered.

From behind her, Yelly's confused voice asked in earnest, "Mama, why didn't we get a card? Is Papa dead?"

"I don't think so, *schat.*"

Despair quickly shifted to renewed hope. Yelly turned to Hilda behind her and passed it on. "Mama said maybe Papa's alive!"

Hilda leaned back to Anneke and announced, "Papa's alive!"

Anneke got very excited. "Papa! Where's Papa?"

Flor gathered her rain-soaked children. "We must keep believing, children. We must not stop praying."

The rain intensified and drowned out the women's sobbing.

By Flor's feet, a fallen, smudged *DECEASED* card drifted by, floating on the tiny stream of tropical rain that snaked across the quickly abandoned field.

～

IN JUNE 1945, THE WOMEN WERE NOTIFIED IT WAS TIME TO MOVE, and again, their destination was unknown.

With little warning they prepared to evacuate. Those assigned to vacate the camp first were forced to leave many of their belongings behind. This proved to be a blessing to Flor. Assigned to the last group, she snatched the opportunity to salvage items and discarded clothing. Hastily, she crafted "shoes" for the children from sneakers and crocheted pillows.

The attractive little shoes proved to be great foresight. The Giliam children wore them on the long trek by foot from the train station to their next destination — Lampersari Internment Camp in Semarang, Central Java. Most of the other prisoners were forced to walk barefoot, on burning asphalt. Women and children who still had footwear were spared excruciating pain and were the envy of many.

On their approach, Flor and the others could see Camp Lampersari positioned high on a hill, wrapped in barbed wire and bamboo fencing. Within its walls were beautiful European homes annexed by the Japanese. A long line of prisoners waited to be admitted at the gate.

Lampersari Semarang had been a flourishing upscale colonial neighborhood, and an enviable expression of Dutch achievement in East Indies trade. Characterized by elegant Dutch-style homes, it was now pitted with internment barracks, a central kitchen and a small hospital. A heavily guarded entrance received the arriving Solo camp prisoners. Flor and her girls, along with Mieke and Inge, were among the hundreds of women approaching its gates.

Flor was suddenly gripped with fear. *What dangers will we face in this place?* Each new location seemed to have its own set of unimaginable challenges.

"Tomarei! Kensa suru (Halt! Inspection)!" commanded the Japanese guard. His piercing black eyes scrutinized the newcomers.

A broad-framed European woman with graying, bobbed hair and a drab, faded dress inspected the women with cold mechanical efficiency.

Mieke's body trembled. Reluctantly she stepped forward in preparation for what had become routine. New internees were customarily body searched before admittance into an internment camp. Mieke spread her arms sideways while keeping her eyes concealed under her helmet.

Inge, Flor and the rest of the children waited nervously as the inspector patted Mieke's bosom, then frisked her lean body. The inspection was thorough, even invasive. Women's undergarments were not off limits. Suddenly the probe stopped. The forbidden lump of Indies Guilder notes burrowed in her underwear had been discovered!

Shaking with fear, Mieke retrieved the contraband from under her skirt and handed it to the inspector with a trembling hand. "Please! Pleeeeese! I'm so sorry!"

A Japanese guard struck her with his rifle butt, sending her crashing to the ground. Her helmet spiralled from her head and bounced away as more blows landed. Flor and the children looked on, powerless, traumatized by the violence. Yelly grabbed Inge and held her close, covering her eyes. Jantine, Anneke and Ineke wailed in terror. The guard hoofed Mieke's battered form several times, clutched his rifle and marched back to his inspection post.

In agony, Mieke lay on the ground bleeding, her ordeal adding to the tension at the gate.

Flor was next. She whispered a quick prayer, *Oh please, God. Please don't let them find the money.* Aware her fear could betray her, Flor avoided eye contact. Swallowing hard, she straightened her back to feign composure and stepped forward. Flor's heart pounded with such force she was convinced the inspector could see it through her flimsy dress.

Yelly and Hilda huddled near each other as their mother extended her arms. Fearfully, they eyed the inspector's every move as she searched Flor from her shoulders, past her waist and down to her hem. The inspector stepped back. Nothing!

Flor dropped her arms, looked at the ground and panted. A cold sweat moistened her sun-bronzed brow, yet she maintained her composure.

"Geef me je tas [Give me your purse]!" the inspector continued.

Flor passed her handbag to the woman. With dread she watched the contents spill onto the inspection table. Spools of colored thread dropped to the ground.

Flor swallowed hard. The woman patted the inside of the purse but failed to detect the money sewn into the lining. Satisfied, she tossed the bag onto the inspection table. *"Verzamel je spullen. Je kunt gaan* [Collect your things. You can go]."

With her head down, Flor nodded slightly and scrambled to pick up the contents of her purse. She felt the notes inside the spools. "Thank you, Father!" she whispered under her breath.

Her traumatized children quietly gathered around her, unaware of how close their mother had come to being caught with money!

Flor tucked her things back into her handbag, and with Inge's help lifted her battered and bleeding friend to her feet. Together the troupe struggled into the already overcrowded camp of eight thousand women and children, hoping Mieke would soon recover from the ordeal.

THE ONCE IMMACULATE COLONIAL HOMES OF LAMPERSARI HAD become a shadow of their former glory. Violated and shamed, they stood imprisoned by overgrown foliage. Their red-tiled roofs, now encrusted with dark mold, reflected neglect, as did the graying white stucco of their formerly elegant facades.

By midsummer 1945, an eerie silence had settled on the camp. Though burdened with a population well beyond its capacity, few voices were heard. Only the broad leaves of the date palms soaring above the homes, rustling in the warm breeze, challenged the buzz of the resident cicadas.

Emaciated and dispirited, the children slumped listlessly in the shade of the trees that lined the streets. Others lay quietly on their bunks, dazed. The people living within the confines of Lampersari were silently starving to death.

Gaunt and sickly, Anneke had been admitted into one of the camp's over-crowded, white-walled hospital wards. She lay languid in her worn nightie, while Yelly perched on the end of the child's wrought-iron hospital bed. The older sister's dress hung loosely from her maturing body over grossly swollen legs — the tell-tale sign of the tropical beriberi disease.

Flor sat next to her daughters on a stool, gently stroking Anneke's brow. *"Lieve schat,* please take another sip. It's delicious warm tea."* She was desperate for her little girl to get some nourishment.

Anneke struggled to lift her head. Slowly, with great strength of will, she took a sip, then dropped her head back onto the stained and graying pillow. Even a small amount of movement exhausted her.

A tear formed at the corner of Flor's eye. She had no emotional reserves to cope with the loss of another child. A quiet prayer formed on her lips as she rocked gently. *"Lieve Jezus, genees mijn kleine meisje* [Dear Jesus, please heal my little girl]."* A miracle from God was again her only hope.

Yelly stood up to look out the shuttered window above Anneke's bed. "Do you think Papa will ever come back?" she queried.

It pained Flor to see Yelly so discouraged. Disease, terror, starvation, beatings and dehumanization had taken their toll on her stalwart fifteen-year-old. And Yelly was not the only one. Many in the camp had given up hope. Flor herself had come close to doing the same, but the prospect of perhaps seeing Menno and Pier again kept her going. She had resolved within herself to keep pressing on. With God's help, she would try to remain hopeful.

The quality of life in Camp Lampersari continued to deteriorate, far surpassing the horrors of Ambarawa. How much longer could the prisoners survive the living hell that surrounded them?

"Who would've thought we'd still be here three-and-a-half years later, heh?" Flor said, voicing her thoughts to Yelly.

"I can hardly remember what Papa looks like," Yelly replied sadly. "Do you think he's still alive?"

"We pray every day, Yeltja. We have to keep trusting ... " Flor tried to encourage Yelly, but her words seemed shallow.

"Everybody's dying, Mama. Maybe Anneke will die too."

"No," Flor replied quickly with conviction. Not for a moment would she entertain the thought. "Your little sister is a very sick girl, but she's also a fighter!"

Yelly turned and nodded. "You're right, Momma." A spark in her blue eyes conveyed that Flor's words had reassured her. They would continue to hope together.

20

AIR MAIL

A year after arriving in Japan, Menno's days of working in the kitchen came to an abrupt end. He was reassigned to fieldwork on a nearby hillside at Sagio Yama, on a cliff above the industrial city of Fukuoka. Along with other Dutch POWs, and a handful of local peasants, he was tasked with the removal of trees and shrubs in preparation for seeding. Though days were long, and the manual labor exhausting, Menno enjoyed the crisp freshness of the air. He had resolved to stay focused on his work, and his soul was at peace.

Sweat dripped from his brow as he leaned his toned body forward to drive a spade into the ground surrounding a shrub. Though not particularly large, the bush was stubborn to uproot. Finally, it pried free, and he tossed it on the pile of dirt beside him. Resting on his spade handle for a moment, he rubbed his calloused hands.

"*Shūjin-tachi! Kyūkei suru* [Prisoners! Time to break]," yelled the guard. "*30-Bun-go ni mōichido yarinaoshite kudasai* [Start again in half an hour]."

Just then Menno noticed a large, winged cockchafer beetle struggling in the dirt near the hole in the ground. With the tip of his spade he flicked the creature into the air and mischievously called out to the Dutch prisoners nearby, "Protein! Come get it!"

Two lanky POWs dove for the beetle as it spread its wings to take flight. After a scuffle in the dirt, one POW victoriously held up the prize, popped it into his mouth and crunched down on the beetle's hard shell. Menno laughed.

The POW who had lost out on the delicacy sidled up to him. "I hear there are bamboo shoots down in the valley, close to the ridge. If we're quick, I reckon we can get there and back before break's over. What d'ya say?"

"Let's go!" Menno welcomed the adventure.

The two men slipped unnoticed into the nearby brush, eager to scour the grassy mounds. It was worth the risk.

Unsuccessful at finding edible shoots, the men wandered closer to the edge of the cliff overlooking Fukuoka. They had heard numerous stories about the impressive industrial city and were curious to catch a glimpse of it below. Never could they have imagined the scene that unfolded before them.

"My God!" exclaimed the POW.

Menno was lost for words. Like matchsticks in continual succession, bombs dropped relentlessly from the squadron of American fighters charging overhead. One after another, the impressive skyscrapers imploded sending great columns of fire and smoke billowing into the air. Fukuoka was flattened before their eyes.

Menno spoke the thoughts racing through his mind, "The war will be over soon."

∼

By August 1945, the young women of Camp Lampersari were required to work on a new road outside Semarang. Yelly and her peers walked barefoot to the construction site each morning, working all day in the scorching sun before returning on foot in the evening. The hard labor was taxing, yet Flor welcomed it. The routine provided the girls with an extra meal each day and gave them a diversion as well as a sense of purpose. *That's far better than languishing in idleness and despair,* she reasoned.

One day Yelly returned to camp excited. "Mama, you know what I just saw? On the guardhouse at the gate, there's a sign that says, 'May 5, 1945 — HOLLAND LIBERATED'. Could that be true? Is the war over?"

Flor felt a surge of hope. "May 5? That's three months ago." Were these really their final days of captivity?

"I guess ... it could be true," she reflected, "unless it's just another cruel joke." Flor knew the tactics of the Japanese. "If the war is over, or almost over, we need to be *flink* [brave], Yelly. And patient."

The news made Flor even more determined that she and her children would survive the war, but what about Anneke who suffered terribly from cholera. How could she live much longer without eating? Her intestines had begun to protrude whenever she attempted to digest even the slightest bit of food, and Flor routinely pushed them back in. Anneke was becoming weaker by the day, yet Flor was resolved not to give up.

Soon the insatiable camp rumor mill circulated the news that the war in Europe had ended. Germany had signed a document of unconditional surrender on May 8, 1945, and it now remained for Japan to do the same. They would later learn that the Japanese, however, rejected the *Potsdam Declaration* issued by the Allies on July 26, 1945. The notice demanded Japan's unconditional surrender and threatened "prompt and utter destruction" should their terms be refused.

~

MEVROUW DE BOER, A TALL, SKINNY WOMAN IN HER FIFTIES, WITH graying, tousled hair, stealthily crept toward a camouflaged brown lizard resting in the shadow of a Lampersari home. Steady and determined, she slowly lifted a metal pot above her head. Bordering on madness, her deep-set brown eyes betrayed her desperation. Her lips drawn back in a grimace of concentration exposed cracked, black and decaying teeth.

The creature spotted the looming figure too late. The pot crashed down around it. "Caught you, *grote jongen* [big boy]! Ha ha! Thought you'd get away! Heh!" She jabbered in excitement, her laughter hearty and wild. With bare, crusty hands she snatched it up and strangled it to death.

With a furtive glance, the *mevrouw* was convinced she was alone, but she wasn't. Flor had been watching for Yelly to return from the construction site and could see her neighbor's erratic movements through her window.

Mevrouw de Boer picked up the corpse and crept near Flor's house. Quickly she gathered sticks and leaves among the shrubbery and built a small fire. With stick in hand, she sat down on a stump and carefully skewered the lizard. She was ready to cook her lunch over the sputtering flames.

Before long the aroma of roasting flesh wafted beyond the fire pit. It wound its way past the houses and into the street. A small group of women and children promptly followed the scent to the pit.

"*Mevrouw,* gonna share with the rest of us?" queried a pathetic, gaunt woman.

"Don't be foolish!" chided another. "If the Japs find out, it will bring trouble to all of us!"

"*Ruikt heerlijk Mama* [Smells so good Mama]!" chimed a young boy.

Flor watched the crowd jostle closer. As new arrivals elbowed in to see, some became angry. Shoving gave way to shouting until chaos erupted. Crazed with starvation, the *mevrouw* stood up and shook her stick threateningly at the crowd, her eyes ablaze. "Don't come any closer!" she warned. "He's mine!"

The crowd gasped and moved back, but her momentary sense of empowerment proved fleeting. Flor looked on horrified as a Japanese guard approached from behind the *mevrouw*, raised his rifle, and with a loud crack brought the weapon down across her shoulders. Barely missing the fire pit, the *mevrouw* folded and toppled at his feet.

The guard's heavy boot kicked her repeatedly. With quivering hands, *Mevrouw* de Boer unsuccessfully tried to shield her head.

The gawkers instantly scattered. Breathless with exertion, the angry guard yelled after the receding remnant, "Everyone will be punished!" The bloodied woman lay weeping bitterly while he ground the charred, smoking remains of her lizard into the ashes under his boot.

With her hand over her mouth, Flor receded from the window appalled. "This is not going to end well!"

~

"Too many!" the Japanese foreman at the Sagio Yama exclaimed at the sight of American warplanes overhead.

It was the summer of 1945, and Menno and the POW field workers now saw them on a regular basis. Sometimes up close.

One day American planes dove on the POWs as they marched in line to work in the fields. The Japanese guards escorting them quickly scrambled for cover, but the POWs yelled and flailed their arms at the planes. The American fighters swerved then departed without attacking. Was this a sign that the war was coming to an end? They were cautiously hopeful.

In the days that followed, the Japanese began bracing themselves for a possible defeat. Fearing the POWs would turn against them, they reassigned the men to dig deep trenches — a job Menno dreaded. Two large drums of gasoline and a heavy machine gun were positioned at each entrance and exit. The Dutch were promptly ordered to take cover in the trenches at the sight of American planes.

The growing anxiety among the Japanese was obvious to the POWs, but with no outside information, they lacked awareness of the war's progress. Eventually the Dutch prisoners learned many details. The Americans had captured the island of Okinawa, including an air base the Japanese touted as impregnable, resulting in the increased sightings of American planes.

The location of the coal mines in Nakama positioned the Dutch prisoners one hundred and seventy-three kilometers southwest of Hiroshima, and only one hundred and forty-one kilometers north of Nagasaki — between two major US targets. They were in the midst of a historically unprecedented act of war — the use of the atom bomb.

Twelve thousand kilometers away, the USS Augusta sailed toward the USA, returning from the Potsdam Conference in Europe. Inside Harry S. Truman was minutes away from addressing the nation.

The US president had weighed the options — continue bombing Japan in conjunction with a massive, costly ground invasion, or use a newly developed weapon in hopes that it would end the war. Truman had made up his mind.

∼

ON THE MORNING OF AUGUST 6, 1945, HIROSHIMA BECAME THE first target. Sixteen hours later, the US president announced it to the American people:

A short time ago an American airplane dropped one bomb on Hiroshima and destroyed its usefulness to the enemy. That bomb has more power than twenty thousand tons of TNT. The Japanese began the war from the air at Pearl Harbor. They have been repaid many fold, and the end is not yet ... If they do not now accept our terms, they may expect a rain of ruin from the air, the likes of which has never been seen on this earth ... [1]

Three days later, the Americans dropped an atomic bomb on the coastal city of Nagasaki.

According to the history books, the attacks halted the machinery of war as Truman had hoped. The cities were so completely devastated that Japan's Emperor conceded defeat on August 14, 1945.

Several days passed before rumors began to circulate throughout the POW camps. One of the mine workers overheard a Japanese guard say, "The war is finished." No one dared believe him until the unimaginable happened. American military aircraft swooped overhead and dropped thousands of pamphlets. Little papers with heavenly messages fluttered into the hands of exuberant POWs: *Japan has surrendered unconditionally.* It was official! The war was over!

The POWs were cautiously optimistic, believing that celebrating in enemy territory could be dangerous. Instead, what followed surprised them. Their oppressive taskmasters suddenly became deferential and friendly.

The thrill of freedom brought mixed feelings for Menno. The horrible ordeal was finally over, and against overwhelming odds — at every formidable juncture — he had emerged a survivor. Hundreds of thousands of Allied soldiers and innocent civilians, both Allied and Japanese, had not been so fortunate. His heart broke for their families. The sweet day of victory would bring them even more sorrow.

Immediately he thought of Flor and the children. Were they still alive? How had they weathered the war? Though home seemed a world away, Menno was determined to get back to his family by any means possible.

By the end of August, American aircraft flew over the POW camp with their cargo holds open. Menno and his comrades watched as large drums attached to multicolored parachutes floated down upon them. Inside they found an assortment of food — chicken, potatoes and vegetables. Within a week of liberation, starvation and suffering seemed a nightmare of the distant past. *How quick we are to forget,* Menno mused.

With renewed strength and freedom, the POWs were eager to explore the Japanese countryside. They boarded trains in all directions to discover the exotic sites of the land. Menno found the Japanese people particularly fascinating. He was genuinely impressed with their neat, clean and well-managed schools and took every opportunity to tour them.

Eventually, the Allies finalized arrangements for the POWs' long-awaited trip home. For Menno, it meant a six thousand kilometer journey through seas still dangerously replete with mines. What would he find when he returned home? His future was fraught with uncertainty. He sensed a very different world awaited him.

THE WOMEN AND CHILDREN OF CAMP LAMPERSARI STOOD, scorched by the hot tropical sun, from early morning until evening. As punishment for the lizard incident, those who lived in homes on the same street as *Mevrouw* de Boer had been sentenced to stand on the large sports field for an entire week.

The children were lined up behind their mothers in order of age, with the exception of Flor's family. Flor's back had been gripped with painful spasms, making it impossible for her to stand. Yelly took the lead, Hilda stood behind her, then Ineke. Four-year-old

Jantine followed at the rear. Next to Yelly stood Mieke, with Inge behind her. Anneke remained in the hospital still battling for her life.

On the second day of punishment, the Japanese commander ordered the beaten and mentally broken *mevrouw* to be put on display in a small bamboo cage before the prisoners.

Head tucked between her knees, dried blood caked on her skin-and-bone frame, she sat in ripped undergarments — her only covering. Her arms wrapped instinctively around her legs.

On the previous day, the heavy-set commander had appeared content that the torturous conditions had inflicted satisfactory punishment on the prisoners as he strutted arrogantly up and down the rows. On this day, however, his countenance had fallen and he appeared unusually preoccupied. He paced back and forth nervously, until suddenly he stopped and shouted.

"Dismissed! Go back to your houses," he barked at the group without requesting the customary bow at the end of the field session.

The women and children relaxed and looked around perplexed.

"This is odd," Mieke turned to Yelly.

"Yah. We just got here," responded the fifteen-year-old. "Do you think it's a trick?"

"We don't have to stand anymore?" piped up tiny Jantine appearing beside Yelly.

"We don't, *schat*." Yelly pulled her little sister closer. "Let's go back and see Mama."

The women and children wasted no time returning to the coolness of their residences.

∾

IN THE DARKENED, CRAMPED ROOM THAT HOUSED THE GILIAM family, Flor lay quietly on a stained mattress under the cover of a mosquito net. A persistent bug buzzed outside the mesh, while she studied a page in her pocket Bible. Removing her glasses, she placed the book on her chest and closed her eyes. For several days the muscles in her back had been wracked with painful spasms making it impossible for her to stand. *Maybe this is God's mercy to keep me away from the roll-call*, she thought, yet it broke her heart to think of the suffering her children, friends and fellow prisoners were enduring.

The unexpected sound of happy voices chatting outside suddenly distracted Flor's thoughts. *Could that be the girls?* she wondered. She couldn't imagine why they would be home so early.

Yelly and the three younger girls pranced into the residence, excited to tell their mother the big news. "Mama," cried Hilda, "they told us to go to our rooms!" Yelly explained how roll call had ended abruptly, and added, "The commander even let *Mevrouw* de Boer out of her cage!" The young women had also been excused from working in the fields that day.

"Something significant has happened," Flor said, her spirit surging.

Outside Flor's barrack, they could hear shouting. Hilda darted to the window. "Momma, they are pointing to the sky!"

"What's that sound?" Yelly joined her younger sister.

The family gathered by the window and soon detected the unmistakable drone of distant engines. They could see a small group of women gathering on the field.

"Look over there," a woman pointed at two specs in the sky and shouted. "I think they're planes! And look, they're heading this way!" Soon two aircraft became visible, advancing rapidly toward the prison camp.

"Lord help us!" another prisoner breathed with incredulity. "Are the jets coming to bomb us?"

The airplanes flew in a low, direct course heading straight for Lampersari until their flagged underbellies became visible. "They're OUR planes!" hollered someone on the field, overjoyed at the unexpected sight of Dutch military aircraft.

As the planes roared low overhead, the unmistakable stripes of the Dutch flag became clearly visible. Suddenly the sky was filled with thousands of leaflets showering down like bits of confetti upon the camp, swirling and spinning before floating gently to the ground.

As women and children emerged from their residences, pandemonium erupted — prisoners screamed, jumped and hugged each other.

From deep within her soul, a woman released a roar of defiance against all the atrocities she had endured, *"BEVRIJDING* **[FREEDOM]!"**

The streets were filled with sounds of celebration and ecstatic joy.

Mieke, Yelly and the children rushed outside to join the crowd. Flor pulled herself up to the window and smiled as she watched the children grab the papers falling from the sky. Two women tussled over the same pamphlet, while another stood eyes closed and arms raised. A few children waved at the Dutch planes as they disappeared into the distance.

Mieke grabbed a leaflet and read, *"Japan has surrendered! The war is over! YOU ARE FREE!"* She gasped and stared at it. "Free!" she shouted. With tears of joy she hugged and kissed her elated Inge.

Ineke, not having understood, asked, "Tante Mieke. What does it say?"

In tears, Mieke bent over, placed both hands on Ineke's cheeks and looked lovingly into the little girl's enquiring eyes. *"Lief klein*

261

kind [Lovely little child]! THE WAR IS OVER! We are going HOME!"

Flor watched the commotion from her room — people hugging, laughing and some standing dazed. Tears filled her eyes. Freedom! Finally! It was like a dream!

Yelly and Hilda ran about, squealing with delight, collecting as many pamphlets as they could catch from the sky. But where were the Japanese soldiers? Curiously, not a single guard was in sight.

For some time, the women continued celebrating. Some fell to the ground and wept.

The long-awaited day of liberation had come. They had lived to see it! But would Anneke?.

WITH LOADED RIFLES HELD CLOSE TO THEIR CHESTS, TWO YOUNG Japanese soldiers stood guard at the front doors of the Lampersari Camp hospital. Flor, leaning on Yelly's arm, limped slowly and painfully toward them. In the desperate mother's hand was a freedom leaflet — the token of her new status and rights. She waved it before the skittish guards to indicate that nothing would stop her from seeing her little one. She was determined that Anneke needed to hear the good news.

Yelly by her side, Flor entered the overcrowded, white-walled ward fearing that her precious daughter might have deteriorated even further.

"Lieve schat, alles komt goed [Lovely darling, everything is going to be alright]," she said quietly.

Her back pinched with pain as she sat down slowly on the edge of Anneke's bed. "Annie, the war is over!"

Worry creased Flor's face. Anneke must make it. Tenderly she stroked her eight-year-old's ghostly-white forehead and spoke again. "You, *kindje* [little child], are going to get better, and we are all going home!"

A wonderful thing happened. Anneke's eyes opened. She looked first at Flor and then at Yelly. A big smile formed on her lips almost as if she was expecting the news.

Flor and Yelly looked at each other and burst into tears. Gently Flor held her little girl in her arms and rocked her. As she kissed Annie's forehead, Flor reassured herself, *Alles komt goed* [Everything is going to be alright].

Back at their residence, later that afternoon, Flor re-read the leaflet, devouring every word. Peace and joy, like sunshine, dispelled the oppressive darkness they'd known for so long. What a relief! A bright future lay before them.

Immediately, her thoughts shifted to Menno and Pier. Would she see them again?

∾

THE HOPE OF GOING HOME WAS A TURNING POINT IN ANNEKE'S recovery. She slowly began to get stronger. The unexpected arrival of Dr. de Jong, the Giliam family's former missionary doctor and friend was another boost. Delighted to have Anneke as one of his patients, he made her a priority on his daily visits and often brought special treats such as condensed milk, or eggs. Her strong will and optimism hastened her recovery, along with the surplus of nourishing food, so much so, that she had no interest in ever eating another egg again!

Liberation brought increased food resources for everyone. The daily ration of one bowl of rice per person immediately became two. Quantities of raw food arrived continually, spurring the women to devise creative ways to cook without conventional pots and pans. Soon there was no limit to the quantity of food survivors were permitted to eat. They gorged voraciously.

When the Chinese Red Cross arrived to distribute food packages, they found Lampersari Street buzzing with activity. The internees willingly waited for them in long lines that often wound around the buildings.

Flor stood quietly in line, deep in thought.

"Mama! Mama!" cried a somewhat familiar voice.

Flor jolted from her daydream and scanned the passers-by but recognized no one. Had she imagined the voice? Suddenly the crowd parted revealing two skinny, blond teenage boys with shoulder-length hair, filthy and matted, wearing dirty clothes pitted with holes. Their appearance shocked her.

"Mama! Mama!" Again, one of the boys yelled and ran toward her.

"Pier?" Flor gasped in amazement and cautious hope. Not only his appearance, but his voice had changed!

"Pier! It *is* you!" she exclaimed. Two long years had passed since she had seen her son, and every day she had dreamed of this moment. Flor hugged and kissed her fourteen-year-old, now taller than her.

"Ouch!" She recoiled abruptly. Something had bitten her. She scratched the spot on her arm and pressed in to take a closer look at her son. Pier was covered with crawling lice! Flor cupped his face in her hands and looked into his eyes. "Pier, when was the last time you took a bath?"

He made a quizzical face and shrugged.

"Well *jongen*, you're about to get a good scrubbing!" she bustled with motherly authority. "And this hair is coming off!"

They both laughed, and Flor gave her son another warm embrace, despite the lice. Her beloved Pier was back! God had answered her prayers!

Their reunion was brief. Pier was promptly ordered back to Ambarawa because he and a friend had left the camp before their official release.

When Flor was eventually notified to pick him up, she decided to stay back to take care of Anneke, who was still recovering. In her place, she assigned Yelly to go with Mieke and Marjan.

When the women arrived at their former internment camp, they were appalled. It had deteriorated into chaos. Even basic hygiene was non-existent. Most shocking was the news that all the older men who had replaced the women and children had perished — every one of them.

Yelly, Pier and the others returned to Lampersari with word of new danger: Sukarno and his followers had declared the Dutch Indies a republic, igniting a war of independence. In a bizarre twist of fate, the soldiers who had been their oppressors now became their protectors. Their former prison, gated and secured, kept the rebels away. Women and children again found themselves captive, now for their own safety against islanders determined to eliminate the Dutch — once and for all.

---

1. President Truman Speech After the Bombing of Hiroshima, August 6, 1945. Link: c-span.org/video/?294914-1/president-truman-speech-bombing-hiroshima

21

SPECIAL DELIVERY

ISLAND OF KYUSHU, JAPAN, SEPTEMBER 1945

"Hey, Giliam!" Menno turned in the direction of a familiar Japanese-accented voice on the crowded Nakama train platform. "I bet you're happy now!" hollered the youth from across the tracks. Surprised yet delighted, Menno spotted Matsumo. He lifted an arm to wave back, but his former student disappeared into the crowd.

What are the odds of that? Menno reflected momentarily as he patted the military duffle bag slung over his shoulder. His precious letters to Flor were buried safely inside and he had Matsumo partially to thank for that. He prayed that his influence on the young Japanese soldier had been positive.

Thanks to the United States military, Menno was on his way home. In an elegant passenger train bearing a Dutch flag, he travelled to his first destination — the coastal city of Nagasaki.

Menno watched through the window in shock as villages, cities and factories all destroyed by war, passed by. As the train approached the station in Nagasaki, he witnessed the catastrophic impact of the atomic bomb. The once thriving city had been incinerated and reduced to rubble and debris. As far as

Menno could see, every building had been flattened except one — a tiny church.

At the railway station, the men were allowed to walk about, but were warned not to go too far because of the bomb's contamination. Most disturbing was the spectacle of pathetic, wandering souls picking through the rubble. Menno rummaged through his bag to find something to give the children. "Chocolate bar?" he asked, offering a treat to a young boy. The child met his gift with vacant eyes and an expressionless face. *"Father help him survive,"* Menno prayed, his heart breaking.

In the processing center at the railway station, Menno, along with his former POW compatriots, was required to shower, be disinfected, and exchange his old clothes for new ones. Next, they were all taken to an American naval ship heading to Okinawa — one step closer to home.

The first morning on board, Menno was invited to play bridge with a group of men. To his amazement, his former, bad-tempered apprentice Henk was among them. Menno joined the game, hopeful the young man had forgotten the hot coffee incident. But he hadn't. Unable to resist, Henk remarked with levity, "Gentlemen, let's remove the coffee from this table. I expect Menno will throw it at us if he loses!"

The ship's approach to Okinawa was sobering. Reminders of the horrors of war were everywhere. Countless masts of sunken battleships protruded from the water and innumerable graves littered the hillsides. The battle of Okinawa, known as Operation Iceberg, had been the scene of the largest number of casualties of World War II. Menno considered those who had paid the ultimate price — more than one hundred thousand Japanese along with the fifty thousand Allies who had fought ... *to win my freedom,* he thought. *How grateful I am to be alive!*

Menno's stay in Okinawa held a bittersweet surprise. It came in the form of a small note written on toilet paper, folded over and fastened with a grain of rice. The fragile note had traveled the great distance from the Indies to Thailand and then to Japan to reach him. He recognized the handwriting immediately. It was Flor's! She had survived!

Menno opened it overjoyed and hastily read its contents: "We are all alive, except Menno. He went to heaven. We live in Semarang."

He sat stunned.

Menno was extremely grateful and overjoyed that Flor and six of his children were alive. So many POWs had received word that their families had perished, and he had witnessed their pain first-hand. Yet he shared that sense of overwhelming grief with the loss of his precious son. What was the cause of Menno's death? How had Flor coped? What were the other children's reactions? Questions tumbled through his mind as the pangs of sorrow gripped his heart.

"He went to heaven." He read the words again. They were clear and unmistakable. His thoughts went back to the memory of his beloved boy singing his favorite song — the one he knew by heart.

> *Daar boven juicht een grote schaar*
> *Van kindren voor God's troon*
> *Verlost van zonden van gevaar,*
> *Tot eer van's Vader's Zoon*
>
> [High in the sky is a tremendous throng
> Of children before God's throne
> Delivered from sin and danger,
> To the honor of the Father's Son]

Menno's thoughts continued, transcending earth and carrying him up to heaven where he envisioned his blond, curly-haired boy with a throng of children singing joyfully around God's throne. His son looked so happy and free.

The scene filled his heart with peace and closure, yet, he knew his family would never be the same.

~

SEVERAL WEEKS PASSED BEFORE THE FORMER POWS RECEIVED notice they would be flown to Manila, Philippines — another city ravaged by war. As in Okinawa, the Manila harbor was a graveyard of sunken ships, their protruding masts representing to Menno flags at half-staff — symbols of mourning.

Upon arrival, the men were transported to a camp thirty kilometers outside the city, where the officials met their every need. No reasonable request was denied, but Menno's heart ached for his family, still two-and-a-half thousand kilometers away. It was here he penned a letter to his parents in Holland informing them that he was alive. *"God, de Heer Heeft mij wonderlijk bewaard en behoed* [The Lord God has wonderfully kept and protected me]," he wrote on October 10, 1945. Menno would later discover that his father, Pier E. Giliam of Boazum, Friesland, had passed away just three months earlier, not knowing if Menno had survived the war.

Next, he traveled to Borneo, the largest island in Asia situated directly north of Java. In the port city of Balikpapan, Menno came face to face with his new reality — he would not be returning to the same Dutch East Indies he had left three-and-a-half years earlier. The colony was now fiercely engaged in a war of independence. Islanders had taken advantage of Japan's surrender, had pillaged the war-torn islands and murdered many Dutch women and children.

Sukarno, the leader of the revolt, had declared his country's freedom from colonial rule and was appointed the first president of the Republic of Indonesia. He was determined to resist Dutch efforts to recolonize the islands until the Netherlands recognized Indonesia's independence.

To avoid an escalation in violence, a British mandate forbade Dutch soldiers to return to Java for political reasons, until further notice. Those with wives and children on the island feared for the lives of their families.

"Now the war is over, and I still can't go home!" Menno complained to a Roman Catholic missionary. "At least there I could protect them."

The man thought a moment and smiled. "While you were working on the Burma Railway, and later when you were in Japan, were you anxious about the welfare of your family?"

"No, not at all," he replied pragmatically. "What could I do? I prayed every day for them."

"And God took care of them," the missionary challenged him. "And now that you're so much closer, don't you think He'll do the same?"

Menno realized the clergyman was right. He chided himself thinking, *Of course, God will take care of them! What happened to my faith?*

∾

CAMP LAMPERSARI HAD METAMORPHOSED DRAMATICALLY SINCE liberation, and Flor basked in its new joyous mood. Once docile and lethargic, the children now ran and played outside, vibrant and happy. Still, foremost on Flor's mind was her concern for Menno. Was he alive? She still hadn't heard from him.

In October 1945 husbands began returning for their wives and children. Through them Flor attempted to glean information about Menno. It soon became apparent that the islander's revolution had delayed many POWs from coming back to Java.

On October 25th, when three thousand dreaded death notices arrived from the POW camps in Thailand, great anguish engulfed the camp.

"*Mevrouw* Giliam!" Flor heard her name. With trepidation, she approached the guard. "There is no notice for you." Flor's heart leapt! Menno may still be alive! She would encourage the children to continue to pray for their father's return.

The following month Flor received a notice of a different kind, and it contained good news. The Giliam family was permitted to leave Lampersari! Travel arrangements were quickly made for their transport by air to Bandung, a large city that promised improved living conditions.

With anticipation, the following morning Flor and the children packed a trunk full of their meagre belongings and hauled it into the back of an army vehicle. Through an open window, Flor took one last look at Camp Lampersari. *We're finally leaving this horrible place,* she sighed. Soon, the camp she would forever associate with the final days of her family's wartime suffering disappeared out of sight.

Upon arrival in Bandung they were transported to a Christian High School where they were assigned living quarters. The school's location outside the city limits, however, made it an easy target for uninvited aggression by islanders. Once again Japanese soldiers served as their guardians, faithfully quelling random attacks and riots.

Living in the confines of the school compound reminded Flor daily of Menno, and their former life at the Mission Home in Gombong. *But where are his students now? Have they changed their attitude toward us? And toward God?* Flor wondered.

It had been five months since the war had ended, and she was becoming anxious.

~

THE YEAR 1946 BROUGHT WITH IT A SENSE OF FRUSTRATION FOR Menno as well. With no formal preparations for him to leave Borneo and return to Java, Menno requested, and received, a formal discharge from the Dutch KNIL army. Civilian status allowed him to open a local school and teach classes with the full permission of the authorities. After years of absence from the classroom, Menno was thrilled to be teaching happy, energetic children who were eager to learn.

Though his work was fulfilling, weeks turned into months with no sign of permission to return home. Menno could wait no longer. He devised a plan.

Every week, he had observed a Koninklijke Paketvaart-Maatschappij (KPM, Royal Packet Navigation Company) boat docking at the harbor in Balikpapan *en route* to Tandjong Priok, Java. Menno and a friend would pose as deck hands and board the ship on the pretense of loading cargo, then stay on as stowaways. And it worked! Without a ticket, money, identification papers or military approval — only their backpacks and a few belongings — they were on their way to Java hidden in the ship's hold.

Menno knew many challenges still lay ahead. How would he travel on the island without money? Would it be possible to navigate territory now engaged in war? He didn't even know his family's whereabouts. *But God brought me this far,* he reassured himself. *Certainly, He will make a way.*

When the stowaways disembarked at the busy port, they tried to hitch a ride to Djakarta on a military vehicle, but without identification, they encountered difficulties. Due to civil war, strict security on the roads was being enforced.

They eventually arrived at the Dutch military base in Djakarta where the officer in charge sharply reprimanded them. "You left Balikpapan without permission? And you're telling me you have no papers?"

"I am a school headmaster and served in the Dutch military out of duty." It was the truth, and Menno spoke with confidence. "The KNIL gave me honorable discharge in Borneo to start a local school."

The officer listened as Menno explained his family's circumstances: the concentration camps, the death of his son, and Flor's
inability to travel with six children to Borneo. Sympathetic
toward him, the officer permitted Menno to stay at the base until
papers could be prepared and arrangements made for his
transport.

Under normal circumstances, Menno would have travelled by
road to Bandung. With part of the city now captured by revolu-
tionaries, the road had become unsafe. The Dutch military was
leery to allow civilians to travel in military vehicles. *Once again,
an impasse,* thought Menno, but he wasn't about to give up.

In the meantime, he discovered a former acquaintance was in
charge of flying regular food supply runs from the military base
to Bandung. Would his friend allow him to fly with him on one
of his flights? It was worth a try.

The pilot listened to Menno's appeal, but could make no
promises. Strictly a cargo carrier, the aircraft was not equipped to
transport passengers. A few days later, however, he summoned
Menno to his office. "Be ready in the morning."

Menno was elated. He rose the next day full of expectation and
arrived early at the airbase to admire the Dakota — an aircraft
that had helped so many during the war. The beautiful, bright
Sunday morning sky spoke of promise.

"She's not pretty, but she *can* fly," quipped the seasoned pilot.
"Hop in, if you don't mind sitting on a sack of flour."

Menno was on his way.

∼

THE SUNDAY MORNING SERVICE AT THE LITTLE DUTCH PROTESTANT
church in Bandung had come to an end, and the children were
released to play. Pier and Hilda were the first out the door.

"Race you to the *knikkeren* pit!" Pier challenged, clutching his colored marbles.

"Wait for me!" cried Ineke.

It had been six months since the end of the war, and the children had bounced back healthy and strong. Flor, in typical fashion, had made sure they were clean and neatly dressed. She held five-year-old Jantine's hand as they neared the church doorway. Anneke and Yelly followed close behind.

Slim and beautiful in a floral dress, Menno's favorite, Flor smiled and extended a hand toward the reverend as he greeted congregants leaving the service. "*Mevrouw* Giliam, any word of your husband's return?"

Flor's eyes saddened. She shook her head.

"I hope you hear soon." His voice was empathetic, but Flor was tired of people asking. She smiled graciously and stepped away.

"You know what I just figured out?" Yelly offered enthusiastically. "Papa left exactly four years ago today!"

"Is that so?" The words were more like a stab to Flor's heart than useful information. "It's the seventeenth ... of February?" She asked wistfully.

"Yes, Mama. I hope Papa comes back soon. Living in the school feels like we're still in camp."

The rumble of a small airplane on course to land at the Bandung airport caused Flor and her three daughters to look upward. Flor pointed at the plane and said jokingly, "Maybe Papa is in there and on his way to us!" The younger children giggled and danced around, enjoying the thought.

Flor had tried hard to stay optimistic, but the wait was becoming unbearable.

On the way home she and the girls passed the children absorbed in their *knikkeren* game. Pier held up his favorite marble and announced, "Watch me! I'm gonna win!" He rubbed the red stone in the palms of his hands and flicked it into the game.

"Children, come. Don't dirty your good Sunday clothes," beckoned Flor. "Let's go home for dinner."

Pier scored! Arms raised, he jumped up cheering. The children reluctantly heeded their mother's directive and scooped up their marbles to follow her.

"Home" for the Giliam family was a white-walled classroom with mattresses on the floor. Flor and Yelly had started making a meal when Pier appeared, his hands behind his back. "For you, Mama!" He produced a haphazard bunch of tiny white flowers.

Delighted, Flor inhaled their delicate scent and received the bouquet, but wrinkled her brow with feigned disapproval. "Pier, where did you get them? Not out of someone's garden, I hope?"

Her son shrugged and grinned broadly with a guilty sparkle in his eyes. She adored him and the gesture. Her disapproving furrowed brow quickly gave way to a smile. The sweet fragrance would add freshness to their home.

"Girls, go see if the neighbors have a vase we can borrow." Anneke, Ineke and Jantine jumped at the opportunity to help. They dashed out the door.

"Here! Girls shake out the tablecloth while you're at it!" Flor called after them, but it was too late. They were gone.

Across the school campus, Menno shook the hand of the director who had pointed him in the direction of the temporary family housing. "*Dank u meneer* [Thank you sir]," he said, his heart pounding.

Would his family be there? Would the children still recognize him? He proceeded with apprehension.

Three blonde, young girls skipped toward him as he crossed the campus grounds. Could they be his daughters? "Pukkie!" He called out his favorite nickname.

The girls eyed the unfamiliar tall man and hastened their pace. They knew better than to speak to a stranger.

Menno shook his head. They seemed so familiar. He continued into the school, turned a corner and headed toward the classrooms.

Flor stepped into the hallway, on her way outside to shake the tablecloth. Suddenly she stopped. A rush of heat coursed through her body. "Menno?"

There he was, walking straight toward her, a man of stature, tanned and slender.

"Flor?" Menno asked, incredulous.

"Menno!" Flor rushed to him as he scooped her light frame into his arms kissing her tenderly. They wept in each other's embrace.

Unable to take his eyes off his wife, Menno set her down on a hall bench. "You look so young and innocent," he said softly.

Flor stared searchingly at her husband — his dark curly hair now peppered with a few more grays, the gentle lines on his forehead deeper. Yet there was more. *He seems gentler — even kinder*, she thought.

"You don't look so bad yourself!" They both chuckled.

Then Flor remembered. Her face fell; her joy replaced by raw pain. "Your son ... Menno," she hesitated. "He ... I'm so sorry!"

She began sobbing, but Menno's eyes remained soft.

"Flor, you are even more beautiful than I remember. You seem — taller? Stronger? Something. You've changed."

Flor couldn't hear his words. She needed to unlock what had been hidden in her heart for so long. "Menno ... he called to me. I ... I tried ... but I ... I... " Grief welled up.

She tried again, swallowing hard. "I wasn't there for him when he died!"

Menno tenderly caressed Flor's face. *"Oh, lieve schat.* What you've had to carry all these years!" He was sympathetic and loving. "But I have you, and we have each other. *Alles komt goed* [Everything is going to be alright]."

Flor buried her head into his broad chest. This was the moment Menno had dreamed of for four long years. Flor was back in his arms. He was finally home!

Suddenly Yelly appeared in the hall looking for Flor and immediately recognized her father. She rushed to embrace him, but Menno balked. His eldest daughter, only eleven-years-old when he left, had matured to look–more like twenty, and he didn't recognize her. He pushed her away.

In shock and rejection, Yelly recoiled. This was not the reunion she had envisioned. Flor quickly reached for her hand and drew her back to her father.

"It's Yelly," she said gently to Menno. "Why don't you give her a kiss?"

"Yelly?" Menno was astounded by her transformation. "You're all grown up! He pulled her close and wrapped his arms around her.

Flor wanted him to know the goodness of Yelly's character and what an enormous support she had been. "Yelly helped me tremendously all these years. You should be very proud of her," she said. Would she ever be able to fully explain it to him?

Menno's eyes filled with tears as he looked into the beautiful face of his grown daughter. Then Hilda, Anneke and Jantine burst around the corner, full of excitement, mirth and conversation. The sight of the same tall man whom they'd encountered outside stopped them short. Flor, cheered by their arrival, said joyfully, "Papa look! Here are three more of your daughters. Hilda, come! Give your father a kiss."

Hesitantly, Hilda walked forward.

Menno bent toward her. She kissed him lightly on the cheek and stepped back. This was his daughter! A sparkly-eyed thirteen-year-old blossoming into a beautiful young woman. "Hilda, you always gave your papa so much joy!" he said, his eyes moist.

Anneke and Jantine approached holding hands, unsure of the strange man. Flor pulled cautious Anneke close and put her arm around her. "In the last days of the camp," she told Menno, "Anneke was a very sick girl. We thought we might lose her, but she didn't stop fighting. She was *erg flink* [very strong]!"

Menno couldn't express the overwhelming joy he felt in being surrounded by his lovely family once again.

"And this must be my baby Jantine!" he said with deep adoration and wonder. He sat down on a nearby bench to be her height and stretched his hand toward her. "Come. How old are you now, *schat*?"

Jantine looked at her fingers and held them up. "Five!" she announced with confidence. Flor and the children giggled.

Menno gently stroked her wavy blonde locks, then suddenly looked up, as if sensing a presence. There before him stood a tall, lanky blond youth. "Papa!"

"Pier? Look at you!" Menno rose reverently, sizing up his maturing son. Pier had become a fine young man. Lost for words, father and son held each other in a long, passionate embrace.

Shy Ineke suddenly zipped past and into her mother's arms. Menno saw her flash by and released Pier with an eye-to-eye smile and a pat on his back.

"And this," Menno stated with a broad smile, "must be ... Ineke?"

Flor stroked Ineke's head. "Yes, and you know she's quite a storyteller. Kept us entertained in the camp at night." She whispered to Ineke and nudged her toward her father.

The children giggled as Menno slowly sat down. Ineke hesitated momentarily but climbed onto his lap. Suddenly the rest of the younger children leapt toward their father, all vying for his knee.

Papa! Home at last!

> *When he calls to me, I will answer him;*
> *I will be with him in trouble;*
> *I will rescue him and honor him.*

> *With long life I will satisfy him*
> *and show him my salvation."* (Psalm 91:15,16)

PHOTOS

Menno Giliam wrote this letter to his parents, Pier Evert Giliam and Heike Giliam-van der Veen, after liberation and upon arrival in Manilla, The Philippines, Oct. 10, 1945.

Menno Giliam, after liberation and prior to returning to his family on Java, 1946.

Surviving Giliam Family and unidentified friends, 1946. Back Right to Left: Florence, Menno, Pier, male friend 1, male friend 2, Jelly (pronounced Yelly), female friend, Middle Row Right to Left: boy, 1 Hilda, boy 2, Front Row Right to Left: Ineke, Jantine, Anneke.

Menno (age 86) and Florence (age 81), Brampton, Ontario, Canada, 1990.

EPILOGUE

In 1974, my grandparents — Opa Menno and Oma Florence (*née* Fokje) Giliam, immigrated to Canada to live with my family in our suburban, Toronto home. As a ten-year-old I quickly gravitated toward Oma's motherly presence, greatly enjoying the warm cups of tea and freshly baked spice cake waiting for me after school.

Following the evening meal, Opa routinely read from the large, green Living Bible and quizzed my brother, my sister and me. Ever the teacher, Opa was intent on ensuring that his grandchildren grew to love the Scriptures. Strict, yet noble, Opa and Oma were a strong, paternal Christian presence in our home.

Of utmost importance to both my grandparents was that every member of their family knew Jesus. To do so was simple — a child-like prayer inviting Him into their life. Every morning Oma faithfully prayed for her nine grown children, their spouses and grandchildren. The list was extensive, and I was deeply impressed.

On rare occasions "camp time" — the years they spent as WWII prisoners of the Japanese — was mentioned in our home, but never in great detail. Opa and Oma neither complained, nor harbored bitterness for the unimaginable sufferings they had endured. They simply left us their memoirs detailing the four long years of hardship and separation — Opa as a Japanese POW, and Oma interned with seven children on the island of Java.

Only once did I hear Opa mention de Graaf*, his closest POW friend. Hans de Wit*, who sadly, also perished while building the infamous Burma Railroad, came to be known simply as the friend who helped resurrect my grandfather with a cigarette! Although all the other non-Giliam characters, also represented by pseudonyms in this book, were very real people, further information concerning their post-war fate has been lost with time.

After my grandparents reunited on Java in 1946, they searched for their valuables — precious belongings left behind when Oma and the children were forced into Japanese internment camps. All their efforts proved to be in vain. They could not recover a single item. Everything was lost.

Eventually, Opa and Oma and their six remaining children — one of whom was my eight-year-old mother Ineke, sailed to war-torn Holland for physical and emotional restoration and to escape the civil war raging in the Dutch Indies. Expatriates from the Islands who spoke with distinct Indo-Dutch accents, they were not particularly welcomed in their homeland. Their countrymen had also suffered miserably under Nazi occupation, and resources were scarce. Reaction to their return was often harsh and unsympathetic.

The Giliams soon returned to the Dutch Indies, but this time to Makassar on the island of Sulawesi (née Celebes). In December 1949, after four years of military and diplomatic confrontation, the Dutch government recognised the independence of the Dutch East Indies and it became the Republic of the United States of Indonesia. Once again, my mother's family was forced to return to the Netherlands, but this time for good.

After the war, Florence gave birth to Marianne, Johanna and Theo. Her last, and eleventh child Elizabeth died during the first year of her life.

In the late 1970s, Menno and Florence Giliam moved to Guelph, Ontario, and later spent their remaining days at the Holland Christian Homes in Brampton, Ontario.

With arms outstretched and a heart full of praise Menno passed to glory in his 91st year. So fitting for a pioneer missionary who had clung tightly to Psalm 91 during the tortuous days of suffering as a Japanese POW. And the once delicate and frail Florence Giliam, who had repeatedly failed her medical qualifications for overseas missionary service, outlived her stalwart Frisian husband. At age 92, she, too, was laid to rest in Brampton, Ontario, having out-lived three of her children — Menno, Elizabeth and my mother Ineke (2001).

In 2013, I stumbled across the original love letters Opa wrote as a POW while he was forced to build the Burma Railroad in the jungles of Northern Thailand. The tiny notes scratched in pencil fell out of a cardboard box in my sister's basement in Unionville, Ontario. Their sudden appearance was a confirmation to me of the task at hand: to weave together my grandfather's notes and my grandmother's memoirs and bring them to life as a novel and on film.

Early in the process of writing, I came to the realization that the best way to relive the story and the time period — the transition of a free and prosperous society into one oppressed by Japanese occupation — was to present this book as historical fiction. The main characters and historical events are all true and accurate, and I have quoted my grandfather's letters verbatim. I have, however, taken liberty with dialogue, and with the addition of finer social and cultural details — although accurate for the time period.

My prayer is that this story will inspire us never to give up when faced with life's greatest trials, but instead, cling to our heavenly Father and live in the shadow of His Son.

*pseudonym

ACKNOWLEDGMENTS

As I sit on my balcony in Jerusalem, I reflect back to the countless hours spent working from my laptop writing *Shadow of the Sun.*

With earbuds in place, I traveled back to the world of my grandparents — WWII Japanese-occupied Dutch Indies — aided by an endless loop of Chopin. At times I would stop and gaze toward the faint outline of the Dead Sea and the dusty Jordanian hills in the distance. On occasion, a friendly Israeli neighbor on an adjacent balcony, or a child playing in the park beneath, roused me back to the present. I worked from the balcony until Jerusalem's cooler winter evenings brought me back indoors.

With a heart of gratitude, I consider all the people who helped preserve my family's story. Special thanks to my uncle Andre Helmus, husband of Anneke Helmus-Giliam, and to my aunt Marianne Hoorn-Giliam, for all your hard work and dedication. Rita Gerber, née Kok, also contributed time and effort to preserving the manuscript, for which I am grateful.

Thank you to my mother's late brother Pierre Giliam and late sister Tante Jelly van der Werff-Giliam, as well as to my aunts Anneke Helmus-Giliam and Tante Jantina van Arkel-Giliam for being willing to sit in the interviewee's chair to share your hearts and memories — sometimes with tears. Like gems, your recollections brought life, depth and sparkle to the story.

Shortly after my father's passing in 2013, my brother Garry discovered a package of family memoirs while cleaning out my father's estate. Garry was convinced that it was a story waiting to be told, and that I was the one to do it. His words gave me the courage to set about bringing to life our family's survival of Japanese occupied Dutch Indies — as a novel and a film. To Garry and Tracy Blom, and Marisca and John Baldwin — my family, thank you for all your love and support and for continually cheering me on. Stay tuned!

Special thanks also to my cousins Menno and Marian Helmus for immediately recognizing God's *hand* on the vision, and for helping to facilitate the process in every way. Thank you for encouraging your daughters Anna and Julia to help with the research and transcription, and to give the story historical and cultural accuracy. A special 'shout out' to Anna for spending three months working with me in Israel, carefully fact-checking every detail. What a gift!

I am also grateful for the assistance and support I received from my late uncle Prof. Tjitze Baarda, husband of Hilda Baarda-Giliam, Joup and Corrie Blom, and my cousin Hilde van der Werff.

Thank you Katharine Joseph, Steve Bryan, Julie Stahl, Nathalie Charron, Lisa Suroso, Yumi Ishido, Jannie Tolhoek, Annie and John Massey, Somy and Lydia Winardi, Ken and Junko Jansen and the KNIL Museum Bronbeek for your support of this project.

Truth be told, this book would never have happened without the talent of my writing partner Daina Doucet. What a joy to work with a good friend who is not only sensitive to God's leading, but one who tackles her craft with meticulous attention and excellence. Thank you, Daina, for your tireless re-working of the many drafts. How fitting it was for us to polish off the manuscript together during your visit to Jerusalem. My prayer Daina, is that you and your family will share in the joy of the eternal fruit of this story.

Lastly, with a heart of gratitude, I thank the Lord for entrusting me with this very special project. After six years of researching, interviewing, working and re-working countless drafts, I have, at this point, lost track of the hours. Many times, I needed to set the manuscript aside overcome by emotion, after reliving my family's trauma, suffering and loss. The depth of my grandparent's love and their persevering faith in God never failed to inspire me. What a heritage!

May God be glorified by their story — *Shadow of the Sun.*

END NOTES

Chapter 2

- *Wilhelmus van Nassouwe,* The National Anthem of The Netherlands. Public Domain. Link: nationalanthems. info/nl.htm

Chapter 4

- *De Juichende Kinderschaar* (The Cheering Children's Choir) Hymn by Adolf Jacob Hogenbirk. 1880. Public Domain. Link: dbnl.org/tekst/hoog041juic01_01/ hoog041juic01_01_0002.php#hoog041juic01_0001

Chapter 10

- *Wilhelmus van Nassouwe,* The National Anthem of The Netherlands. Public Domain. Link: nationalanthems. info/nl.htm

Chapter 11

- *Daar Ruischt Langs de Wolken (There Rustles Amongst the*

Clouds) Hymn by Johannes de Heer. 1905. Public
Domain. Link: nd.nl/cultuur/muziek/628833/johannes-
de-heer-de-man-die-de-heer-heette-en-de-heer-diende;
kerkliedwiki.nl/Daar_ruist_langs_de_wolken

- *De Juichende Kinderschaar* (The Cheering Children's
  Choir) Hymn by Adolf Jacob Hogenbirk. 1880. Public
  Domain. Link: dbnl.org/tekst/hoog041juic01_01/
  hoog041juic01_01_0002.php#hoog041juic01_0001

Chapter 12

- *Wilhelmus van Nassouwe,* The National Anthem of The
  Netherlands. Public Domain. Link: nationalanthems.
  info/nl.htm

Chapter 21

- *De Juichende Kinderschaar* (The Cheering Children's
  Choir) Hymn by Adolf Jacob Hogenbirk. 1880. Public
  Domain. Link: dbnl.org/tekst/hoog041juic01_01/
  hoog041juic01_01_0002.php#hoog041juic01_0001

Photos

1. Gedenkboek Der Friese Zending 1900 - 1950, N.V.
   Drukkerij (Publishing) "De Motor" Sneek, Friesland,
   1950, public domain.
2. Australian War Memorial, public domain.
3. Used by permission: The Netherlands Institute for
   Sound and Vision.

The Internet addresses and website content referred to herein are
accurate at the time of publication (or as of the date specified).
The publisher and author do not endorse all of the content on all
websites cited or promise the permanence of such websites or
any content contained therein.

ABOUT THE AUTHOR

Marney Blom is a Canadian journalist and served for twelve years as the Middle East foreign correspondent for *Acts News Network* (www.actsnewsnetwork.com).

A graduate of the University of Toronto and Queen's University at Kingston, Ontario, for more than 25 years Marney has produced human-interest news features for radio, television and the Internet. Beginning her career as a reporter/producer for Crossroads Christian Communications, Inc., she has traveled extensively throughout North America, Asia, Europe, Africa and the Middle East.

Marney's work has appeared on *Context: Behind the Headlines, CBN News, Christian World News, Heaven TV7, Israel Vision, TBN, 100 Huntley Street, Mundo Cristiano, Evangelische Omroep (EO), the Faytene Show* and *It's A New Day.* Her articles have been published in *Asian Report, Faith Today, Revival Magazine* and on *Christianity.ca.*

Marney directed and produced the documentary film, *From the River to the Ends of the Earth* and *Between Heaven and Earth* - a journey into the Father's Heart for Israel. She has also written the screenplay *Shadow of the Sun* and is currently working to bring *Shadow of the Sun* to life on film.

The author is the granddaughter of Menno and Florence (aka Flor) Giliam, and the daughter of Ineke Blom-Giliam, all characters in *Shadow of the Sun*.

S O...

Has *Shadow of the Sun* challenged or inspired you?

I would love to hear from you.

Please write to shadowofthesunbook@gmail.com.

~

Coming soon ... the *Shadow of the Sun* movie!

Would you like to see *Shadow of the Sun* come to life on film? We are working to bring this unforgettable story to the big screen.

But we need your help.

Find out how you can join us as we make *Shadow of the Sun* — the movie. Visit shadowofthesun.org/movie.

The adventure begins!

God bless you,
Marney Blom